Pictorial

WOODW

TOOLS AN

Pictorial Guide to

WOODWORKING
TOOLS AND JOINTS

by
H. F. MARFLEET

ROUTLEDGE & KEGAN PAUL
LONDON AND HENLEY

First published 1961
by Routledge & Kegan Paul Ltd
39 Store Street
London WC1E 7DD and
Broadway House, Newtown Road
Henley-on-Thames
Oxon RG9 1EN

Printed in Great Britain
by Redwood Burn Ltd
Trowbridge & Esher

© *Routledge & Kegan Paul Ltd 1961, 1979*

First edition 1961
Second impression 1967
Third impression 1968
Second edition (metricated) 1979

ISBN 0 7100 0177 0

PREFACE

THIS book has been prepared with both the apprentice and amateur worker of timber in mind. Hand methods are used to show the application of as wide a range of tools as possible. To know of the existence of particular tools, and how they should be used, is of great importance, whether it be for a livelihood or pleasure. Particular attention is paid to the sharpening and safe handling of cutting tools.

In a number of instances 'right' and 'wrong' techniques are illustrated which, it is hoped, will influence those who are inadvertently using methods which are dangerous or laborious. The written matter has been kept as short as possible when describing the various operations, tools or materials.

The basis of good workmanship is to use the correct tools and see that they are kept in good order. This, in conjunction with reliable means of holding timber firmly, makes an excellent start to any job.

It has not been possible to show every conceivable operation in a book of this size, but the majority of jobs met with can be accomplished by adopting the methods shown. By using a little ingenuity other methods can also be devised to suit the job in hand, once the reader has observed the principles of woodworking tools and appliances.

My acknowledgments are due to Mr. J. C. Stevens, lecturer responsible for Carpentry and Joinery at the Brixton School of Building, for his kindness in checking this book. His valuable suggestions and comments have also been of great use.

H. F. MARFLEET

November, 1960

CONTENTS

CHISELS AND GOUGES

BORING TOOLS

SELECTING AND PREPARING TIMBER

IRONMONGERY—ASSOCIATED TOOLS AND OPERATIONS

GENERAL WORKSHOP REQUIREMENTS

CLEAN AND TIDY CONDITIONS

THESE are important factors, not only in connection with the working area, but also in the care of tools. Cutting edges, which one has gone to great lengths to sharpen, can be easily damaged by untidy methods. There is a lack of thought when a saw is buried beneath a pile of metal tools. Damaged teeth will mean a lengthy sharpening operation. This is but one instance among many where unnecessary labour could have been avoided, had the bench been tidy. Therefore lay out tools in an orderly manner on the bench and from time to time clean it down. Shavings that have accumulated are the cause of many cross words when a small item becomes covered over and lost to view. Occasionally scrape the surface of the bench, thus removing anything which might damage the face of a finished product laid on it.

Tools not required for immediate use should be placed in racks, drawers or on shelves. Boxes or cupboards are useful to store tools not required for general use and help to promote better working conditions.

In general, keep the workshop tidy. Odds and ends of timber need to be stacked in such a manner that their dimensions can readily be seen. Nails and screws and other small items should be kept in covered containers, but here of course the individual has sufficient scope to prepare such storage facilities to suit his needs.

THE BENCH

A bench which is laid out neatly promotes good work. The tools do not become damaged and they are easily seen when required. An average sized bench for the home is about 1.52m long, 0.61m wide and 0.81m high.

RIGHT

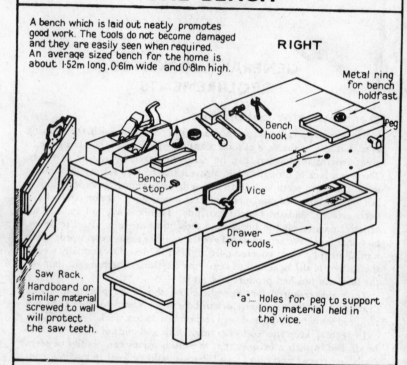

Metal ring for bench holdfast

Peg

Bench hook

Bench stop

Vice

Drawer for tools.

Saw Rack. Hardboard or similar material screwed to wall will protect the saw teeth.

"a".... Holes for peg to support long material held in the vice.

WRONG

Tools jumbled with timber and shavings. Saw teeth, plane irons and any other cutting edge will become damaged if hammers, pincers and the like are heaped over them. Oil spilt on the bench collects dirt and can stain a finished job.

BENCH VICES

An instantaneous grip type of vice with trigger release action is shown. Where the sizes of material constantly vary, this type of vice is an advantage.

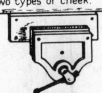

Two types of cheek.

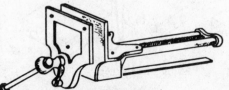

Set the vice 10mm below the bench top. This guards against damage to saws when cutting material in the vice. Ensure that it is perfectly aligned and securely fixed with coach screws.

Hardwood cheeks are necessary to prevent the metal jaws of the vice damaging the work.

The bench chops shown below are not recommended. Their use is very limited.

RIGHT

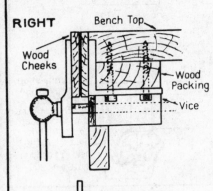

Bench Top

Wood Cheeks

Wood Packing

Vice

WRONG

A vice incorrectly set in the bench will not give a full grip with its jaws.

Maintain the working parts. A wedge behind a trigger that slips, or a piece of barrel to increase leverage, are bad practices brought about because of faults in the vice.

3

BENCH STOPS

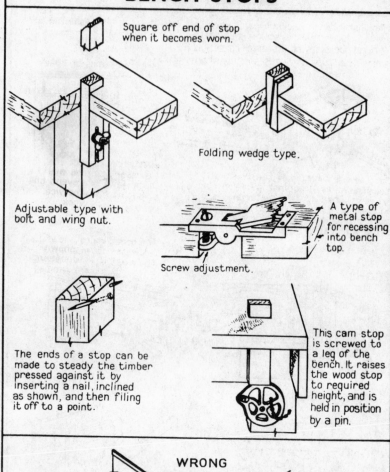

Square off end of stop when it becomes worn.

Adjustable type with bolt and wing nut.

Folding wedge type.

A type of metal stop for recessing into bench top.

Screw adjustment.

The ends of a stop can be made to steady the timber pressed against it by inserting a nail, inclined as shown, and then filing it off to a point.

This cam stop is screwed to a leg of the bench. It raises the wood stop to required height, and is held in position by a pin.

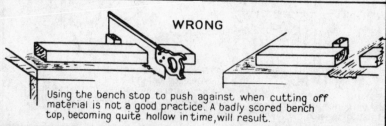

WRONG

Using the bench stop to push against when cutting off material is not a good practice. A badly scored bench top, becoming quite hollow in time, will result.

SAWING AIDS

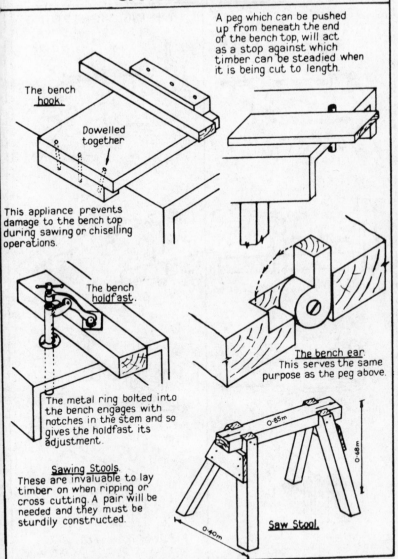

A peg which can be pushed up from beneath the end of the bench top, will act as a stop against which timber can be steadied when it is being cut to length.

The bench hook.

Dowelled together

This appliance prevents damage to the bench top during sawing or chiselling operations.

The bench holdfast.

The bench ear. This serves the same purpose as the peg above.

The metal ring bolted into the bench engages with notches in the stem and so gives the holdfast its adjustment.

Sawing Stools. These are invaluable to lay timber on when ripping or cross cutting. A pair will be needed and they must be sturdily constructed.

0·85m

0·68m

0·40m

Saw Stool.

G. CRAMP SCREW CLAMP AND THUMBSCREW

G. Cramp.
These are popular
for most work.

Securing jobs to the bench,
gluing up etc.

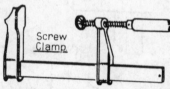

Screw
Clamp

Strong and quickly set to size.

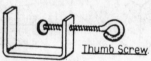

Thumb Screw.

For lightly holding small
members till glue has set.

Protection pieces for use
with the above tools.

WRONG TIGHTENING

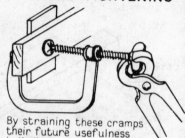

By straining these cramps
their future usefulness
is limited.

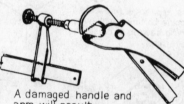

A damaged handle and
arm will result.

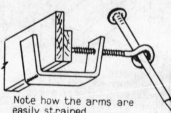

Note how the arms are
easily strained.

Result of not having
protection pieces.- damage to job.

CRAMPS AND CLEATS

Door Cramps.

Light and heavy section T bars are
obtainable. Their lengths vary from 0·60 to 2·10m

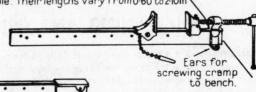

**T Bar
section**

Ears for
screwing cramp
to bench.

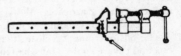

Cramp extension piece.

Sash Cramp - flat bar section.

A light type of cramp.
Not suitable for heavy jobs.

Cramp Heads.

There are various sizes.
A hardwood bar, for preference,
is used to fit them on.

Iron Cleat.

The various lengths are
fitted with a shoe held
in position by an iron
wedge. When gluing up
boards, the pair of folding
wedges are driven tight between
the shoe and edge of timber.

Pair of
folding
wedges.

Wood Cleat.

Made up to suit the
particular job. Used
for the same purpose
as iron cleats.

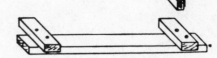

SHARPENING AND GRINDING

SHARPENING is a much abused and disliked operation. It is avoided for various reasons, the main one being the view that, so long as some form of shaving or sawdust is produced from a tool, it cannot be blunt. There is no definite time before having to 'sharp-up' as it depends on the nature of the timber being worked just how long the cutting edge will remain effectively sharp. Refrain from making this edge last for so many hours, days or weeks. If a great effort is required to operate a tool the chances are it requires sharpening. Work becomes so much easier when a tool cuts cleanly and without much effort.

The oilstone must be clean, therefore it is kept in a small hardwood box and covered with a lid when not in use, the waste oil being wiped off from time to time. A mixture of paraffin and machine oils is placed on the stone to prevent its porous surface from becoming clogged with particles of steel produced during the sharpening operation. The importance of sharpening cannot be over-emphasized. Some time spent in sharpening will make work a pleasure, and real enjoyment is sensed when a tool cuts properly.

Grinding is also an essential part of sharpening. It is no easy matter to maintain a reasonable bevel if the edge is too thick. By grinding away the majority of this thick edge to the approved grinding bevel, a much keener and more quickly formed cutting edge will be obtained. For preference use a natural grit grindstone which is kept wet with water from a drip-can. On no account must the steel become hot as this draws the temper. This frequently happens on a grinding wheel when the edge changes colour due to the excessive heat. The blade should constantly be dipped in water to prevent such an occurrence.

OILSTONE AND BOX FOR SHARPENING

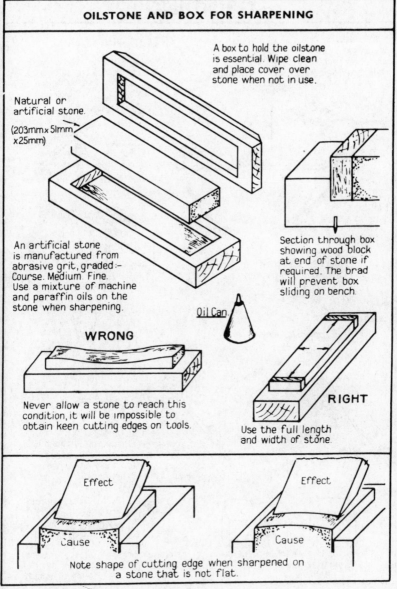

A box to hold the oilstone is essential. Wipe clean and place cover over stone when not in use.

Natural or artificial stone.

(203mm x 51mm x 25mm)

An artificial stone is manufactured from abrasive grit, graded :- Course. Medium. Fine. Use a mixture of machine and paraffin oils on the stone when sharpening.

Section through box showing wood block at end of stone if required. The brad will prevent box sliding on bench.

Oil Can

WRONG

Never allow a stone to reach this condition, it will be impossible to obtain keen cutting edges on tools.

RIGHT

Use the full length and width of stone.

Effect

Cause

Effect

Cause

Note shape of cutting edge when sharpened on a stone that is not flat.

GRINDING

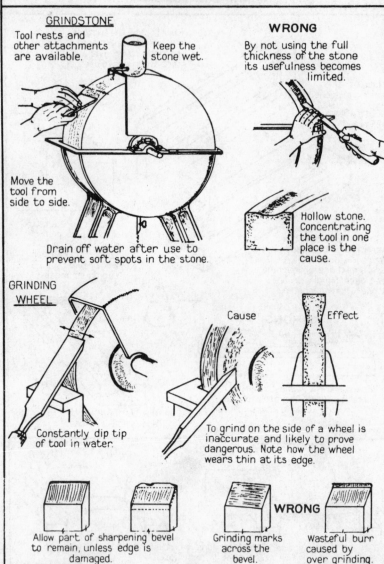

GRINDSTONE

Tool rests and other attachments are available.

Keep the stone wet.

Move the tool from side to side.

Drain off water after use to prevent soft spots in the stone.

WRONG

By not using the full thickness of the stone its usefulness becomes limited.

Hollow stone. Concentrating the tool in one place is the cause.

GRINDING WHEEL

Constantly dip tip of tool in water.

Cause

Effect

To grind on the side of a wheel is inaccurate and likely to prove dangerous. Note how the wheel wears thin at its edge.

Allow part of sharpening bevel to remain, unless edge is damaged.

Grinding marks across the bevel.

WRONG

Wasteful burr caused by over grinding.

TOOL BOX

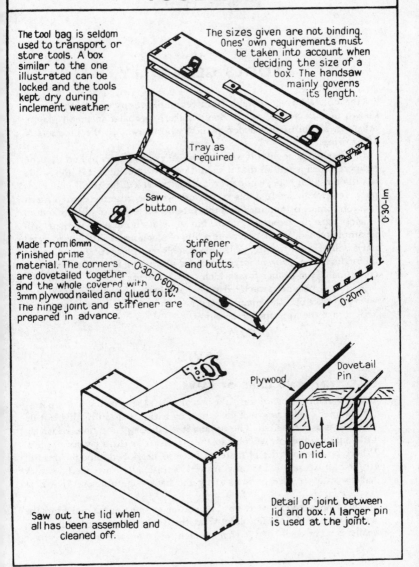

The tool bag is seldom used to transport or store tools. A box similar to the one illustrated can be locked and the tools kept dry during inclement weather.

The sizes given are not binding. Ones' own requirements must be taken into account when deciding the size of a box. The handsaw mainly governs its length.

Tray as required

Saw button

Made from 16mm finished prime material. The corners are dovetailed together and the whole covered with 3mm plywood nailed and glued to it. The hinge joint and stiffener are prepared in advance.

0·30-0·60m

Stiffener for ply and butts.

0·30-1m

0·20m

Saw out the lid when all has been assembled and cleaned off.

Plywood

Dovetail Pin

Dovetail in lid.

Detail of joint between lid and box. A larger pin is used at the joint.

TOOLS GENERALLY

AT the outset buy good tools from reputable shops which stock well-known manufacturers' goods. Some makers specialize in metal planes, others in all forms of wooden planes, whilst saws are the products of other firms.

It is so easy to be put off with 'this is just as good' only to find that the tempered steel is not all that it should be. With soft steel it is impossible to obtain a keen edge, while overhardened steel will break off under impact. Inferior tools are a misery to work with because the desired finish to a job cannot be obtained and this produces a feeling of dissatisfaction.

Most tools are expensive items, but some attention paid to them will be amply repaid. When not in use a film of machine oil wiped over metal parts will prevent rusting, whilst wood tools require coating with linseed oil regularly to prevent dryness or moisture upsetting the balanced condition of the timber from which they are made.

As far as possible associated tools have been placed in groups and, where applicable, the maintenance and sharpening of tools has been kept under the appropriate headings.

SAWS

SELECTION AND CARE OF SAWS

THE saw in most general use is the 650 mm hand saw having 6 or 7 points (to the inch). This saw will cut across or with the grain readily but its chief use is as a cross cut. The ripping it is called upon to do is relatively little but this dual role will obviate the expense of an extra saw for ripping. Where large quantities of material have to be ripped though, the full rip or half-rip saw is the only answer. Thin-bladed saws for fine work have a stiffener incorporated along the back edge and are known as back saws.

Choosing a good saw is no easy matter as one cannot tell from the appearance of the blade (plate) what the quality or temper of the steel really is. The well-tried saw manufacturers who will guarantee their products is the safest solution, but, before buying, a few observations should be made. With hand saws the blade should spring back into a straight line after having been flexed. The straightness of the blade is also particularly important in a back saw. Do not think of buying a saw with a thick blade. Try gripping the handle in the accustomed manner and also make sure that it fits tightly. The balance of the saw will now be noticed. If it does not feel comfortable to hold at this stage, a long time may elapse before one gets that feeling of masterful control when sawing. Lastly, see that the teeth are not damaged in any way.

To prevent rusting wipe the blade with light machine oil or a thin grease. A 25 mm strip of wood grooved to the saw's thickness and tied to its cutting edge will prevent damage when not in use.

RIP, HAND, AND PANEL SAWS

Saws are also known by their length
and number of points to the inch,
seen stamped on the heel of saw.

Toe   87°   Heel

4½ Points

Plan of teeth

HALF RIP SAW
28" long, having
4½ points.
For cutting with
the grain only.

The FULL RIP has larger teeth
but it is seldom used.

Decorative
bead

Straight back

Skew back

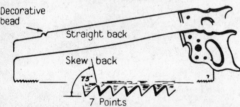

75°

7 Points

Plan of teeth

HAND SAW
Straight and skew back.
They are 26" long with
6 to 8 points.
A general purpose saw
but principally designed
for cross cutting.

PANEL SAW
0·45–0·61m long, having
10 to 12 points.
Useful for cutting plywood,
hardboard and wood of
small section.

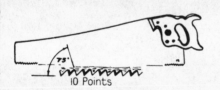

75°

10 Points

To test the quality of a saw,
spring it in this way.
The curve should be regular
and the blade perfectly straight
after it has returned to its
normal position.

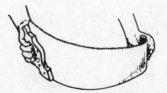

ACTION OF SAW TEETH

In sharpening saws an understanding of the manner in which the teeth actually cut would overcome a number of the usual errors made.

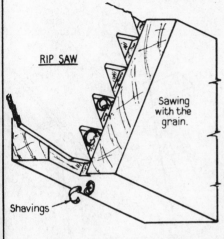

RIP SAW

Sawing with the grain.

Shavings

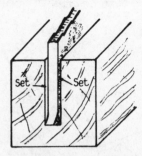

Set   Set

Here the teeth are acting like a series of small chisels cutting a groove. There is a minimum of set because the saw always cuts with the fibres, and binding is not experienced.

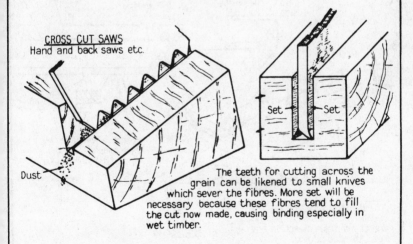

CROSS CUT SAWS
Hand and back saws etc.

Dust

Set   Set

The teeth for cutting across the grain can be likened to small knives which sever the fibres. More set will be necessary because these fibres tend to fill the cut now made, causing binding especially in wet timber.

RIP- AND CROSS-CUT SAWING

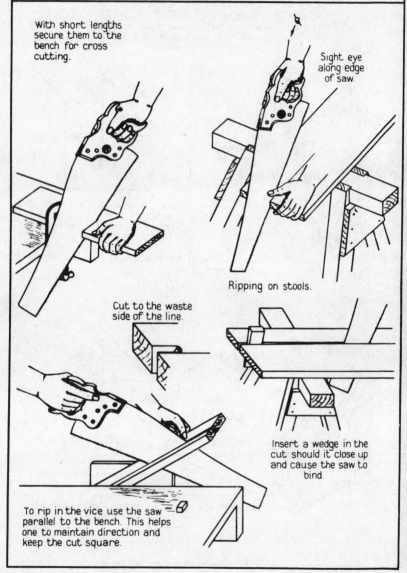

With short lengths secure them to the bench for cross cutting.

Sight eye along edge of saw.

Ripping on stools.

Cut to the waste side of the line.

Insert a wedge in the cut should it close up and cause the saw to bind.

To rip in the vice use the saw parallel to the bench. This helps one to maintain direction and keep the cut square.

PANEL AND TENON SAWS IN USE

RIGHT

To commence a cut, draw the saw towards oneself a few times the thumb positioning it to the line.

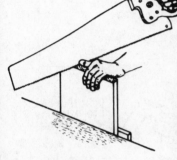

To hold a back saw, point the forefinger along the side of the handle.

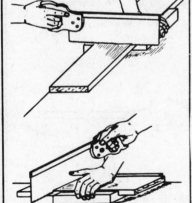

Guide the saw into position with the thumb.

WRONG

Timber too high in vice. Danger of saw jumping.

Stop sawing before the bench is reached.

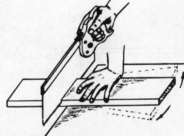

Always hold the timber in a rigid position.

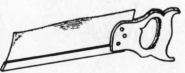

Effect of using a back saw without due care. See above.

BACK SAWS

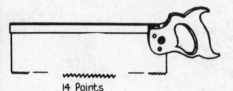

<u>TENON SAW.</u>
0·3m – 0·4m long having 12 or 14 points.

For accurate work in general.

14 Points

<u>DOVETAIL SAW.</u>
0·20 – 0·25m long, 16 to 20 points.

For fine work.

Alternative types of handle.

<u>BEAD SAW.</u>
Similar uses to the dovetail saw but from 0·10m to 0·30m. Very fine work.

The bead saw cutting against the bench hook.

Using the dovetail saw to cut work held in the vice.

All these saws are easily buckled and thereafter spoilt for accurate work. Grip job firmly using a vice or G cramp etc.

BOWSAW

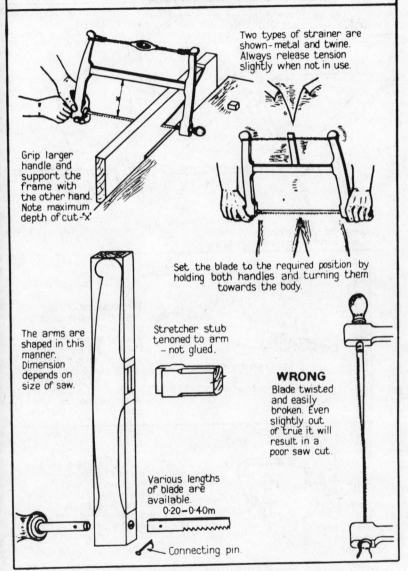

Two types of strainer are shown - metal and twine. Always release tension slightly when not in use.

Grip larger handle and support the frame with the other hand. Note maximum depth of cut -'x'

Set the blade to the required position by holding both handles and turning them towards the body.

The arms are shaped in this manner. Dimension depends on size of saw.

Stretcher stub tenoned to arm - not glued.

WRONG

Blade twisted and easily broken. Even slightly out of true it will result in a poor saw cut.

Various lengths of blade are available. 0·20 - 0·40m

Connecting pin.

COMPASS, KEYHOLE, AND COPING SAWS

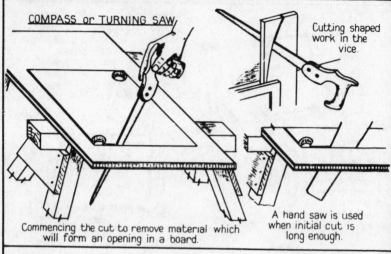

COMPASS or TURNING SAW.

Cutting shaped work in the vice.

Commencing the cut to remove material which will form an opening in a board.

A hand saw is used when initial cut is long enough.

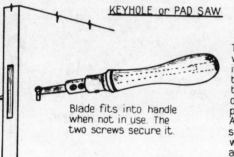

KEYHOLE or PAD SAW

Blade fits into handle when not in use. The two screws secure it.

The blade is discarded when blunt but usually it is because it has become distorted or broken. Therefore leave only just enough blade projecting to do the job. Any of the operations shown on this page can, within reason, be attempted with this saw.

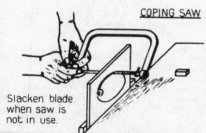

COPING SAW

Slacken blade when saw is not in use.

Suitable for thin material and small work generally. The operation shown is only one of many uses to which this saw can be put. The blade has been passed through the prepared hole and tightened into the frame afterwards.

TOPPING AND SHAPING SAW TEETH

Face towards a good source of light.

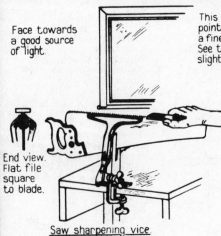

This operation reduces all the points to a common level by using a fine flat file without its handle. See that the edge of the blade is slightly cambered and not hollow.

End view. Flat file square to blade.

Saw sharpening vice.

After topping, flat tops show on the teeth.

Topping filed out. All teeth are now equal in size. Note how part of a broken tooth still remains.

Part of saw chop in detail.

If the file is large enough it will give 3 useful cutting edges.

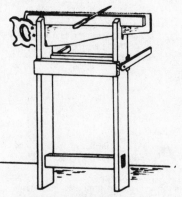

A saw sharpening horse.

Either of these methods may be used to hold the saw during sharpening.

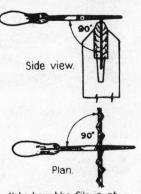

Side view.

Plan.

Note how the file is at right angles to the blade at all times.

SETTING SAW

Holding the saw during the setting operation.

Squeeze the bottom lever taking care not to otherwise move the saw set.

Saw setting is the forcing of alternate teeth in opposite directions. This is because a saw must have sufficient clearance to prevent it from binding in the cut it has made.

The anvil saw set is considered the best and quickest method of setting a saw. In spite of this the spring set is by far the most popular.

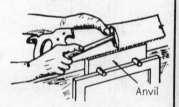

Anvil

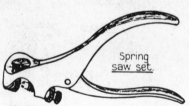

Spring saw set.

The bevelled wheel must be rotated to the number corresponding to the number of points per inch on the saw being set.

Plan view of head of saw set.

Teeth marks

Set

Depth of set, about half of the tooth.

With a new saw take an impression of the teeth before using it. This will be a guide for future reference. Press some of the teeth into a sheet of paper which is resting on a flat board.

SAW SHARPENING

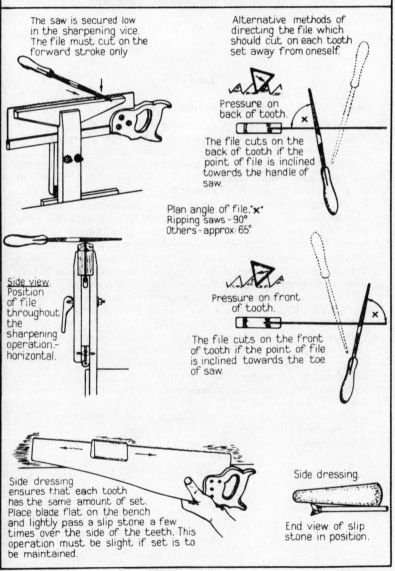

The saw is secured low in the sharpening vice. The file must cut on the forward stroke only

Alternative methods of directing the file which should cut on each tooth set away from oneself.

Pressure on back of tooth.

The file cuts on the back of tooth if the point of file is inclined towards the handle of saw.

Plan angle of file. "x"
Ripping saws - 90°
Others - approx: 65°

Side view. Position of file throughout the sharpening operation.- horizontal.

Pressure on front of tooth.

The file cuts on the front of tooth if the point of file is inclined towards the toe of saw.

Side dressing ensures that each tooth has the same amount of set. Place blade flat on the bench and lightly pass a slip stone a few times over the side of the teeth. This operation must be slight if set is to be maintained.

Side dressing.

End view of slip stone in position.

PLANES

CARE OF WOODEN AND METAL PLANES

THE wooden jack plane is perhaps the most useful of all planes, doing all the rough work, and the only breakable part, should the plane fall off the bench, is the tote (handle) which can be easily replaced.

With all wooden planes ensure that the timber from which they are made is of good quality and free from knots, sapwood and shakes. On the end section the growth rings must be approximately parallel to the sole of the plane, which is the same as saying that the rays, which show as whitish streaks, are nearly square to the sole. When the sole of a wood plane becomes worn it can be trued up easily. The insertion of a new piece in the mouth as this gap becomes enlarged is no difficult matter.

Avoid damaging the plane by repeated hammer blows when attempting to remove an iron. The wedge should not have been driven in so fiercely anyway and gentle taps on the wedge during setting is all that is needed.

To preserve the wood and exclude moisture a pad soaked in linseed oil should be wiped over the exposed surfaces as often as they appear in need of it, this applies especially to the sole.

There are a wide variety of planes made of metal, most of which are fitted with precise adjustments for locating the cutting iron. These require careful handling, because a fractured body, even though repaired, can be out of true. This will cause an unworkmanlike finish to a job when such a plane is used. Spare parts are available from reputable firms but, of course, an expense is still involved. With this in mind pay particular attention to where a metal plane is placed—tools have a habit of being knocked off a bench.

To prevent the metal from becoming rusted wipe an oily rag—machine oil—over the plane occasionally.

JACK PLANE

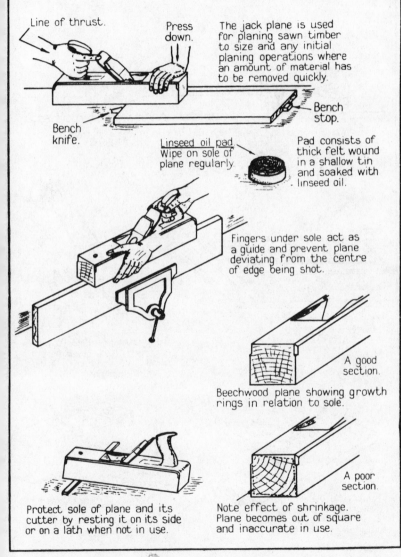

Line of thrust.

Press down.

The jack plane is used for planing sawn timber to size and any initial planing operations where an amount of material has to be removed quickly.

Bench stop.

Bench knife.

Linseed oil pad. Wipe on sole of plane regularly.

Pad consists of thick felt wound in a shallow tin and soaked with linseed oil.

Fingers under sole act as a guide and prevent plane deviating from the centre of edge being shot.

A good section.

Beechwood plane showing growth rings in relation to sole.

Protect sole of plane and its cutter by resting it on its side or on a lath when not in use.

A poor section.

Note effect of shrinkage. Plane becomes out of square and inaccurate in use.

SMOOTHING PLANES

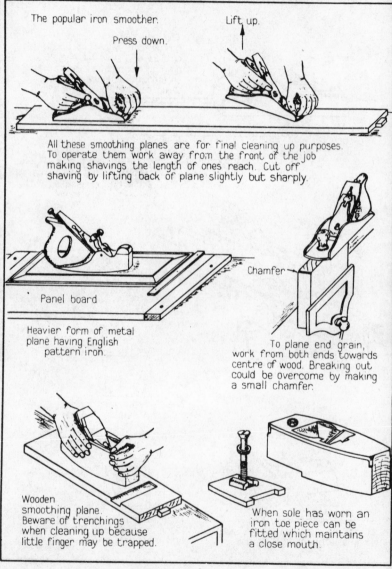

The popular iron smoother.

Press down.

Lift up.

All these smoothing planes are for final cleaning up purposes. To operate them work away from the front of the job making shavings the length of ones reach. Cut off shaving by lifting back of plane slightly but sharply.

Panel board

Heavier form of metal plane having English pattern iron.

Chamfer

To plane end grain, work from both ends towards centre of wood. Breaking out could be overcome by making a small chamfer.

Wooden smoothing plane. Beware of trenchings when cleaning up because little finger may be trapped.

When sole has worn an iron toe piece can be fitted which maintains a close mouth.

SHARPENING PLANE IRONS

Sharpening.

Maintain correct bevel. Keep wrists steady or a rounded edge will result from rocking the iron.

Removing burr.

Lay iron perfectly flat on the stone.

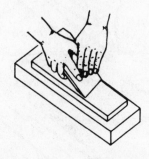

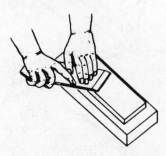

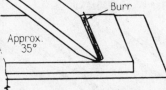

Exaggerated view of the burr formed in the sharpening position.

Burr

Approx. 35°

The iron cannot possibly be sharp until a burr has been formed.

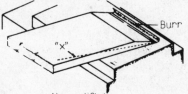

A few rubs and then repeat both processes until burr has gone.

"x"

Burr

Never lift to position "x"

RIGHT

Feel for the burr by lightly drawing thumb away from cutting edge.

WRONG

This will result in a cut thumb.

Rounded edge

A face bevel due to "x" above.

DOUBLE PLANE IRONS

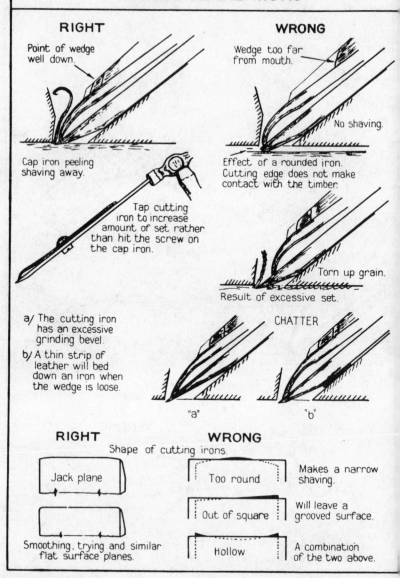

RIGHT

Point of wedge well down.

Cap iron peeling shaving away.

Tap cutting iron to increase amount of set rather than hit the screw on the cap iron.

a/ The cutting iron has an excessive grinding bevel.

b/ A thin strip of leather will bed down an iron when the wedge is loose.

WRONG

Wedge too far from mouth.

No shaving.

Effect of a rounded iron. Cutting edge does not make contact with the timber.

Torn up grain.

Result of excessive set.

CHATTER

"a"   "b"

RIGHT   **WRONG**

Shape of cutting irons.

Jack plane

Smoothing, trying and similar flat surface planes.

Too round — Makes a narrow shaving.

Out of square — Will leave a grooved surface.

Hollow — A combination of the two above.

DOUBLE PLANE IRONS—SETTING CAP IRON

English Pattern.

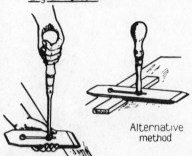

American pattern.

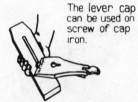

The lever cap can be used on screw of cap iron.

Alternative method

To remove cap iron.

Hold firmly on edge of bench and use a short screwdriver for preference. Remove the cap iron similarly to setting.

It is not necessary to remove this type of cap iron when sharpening. Slide it back a few inches.

SETTING

Slide cap iron over cutting iron and show an approximate amount of set before tightening screw. Tap the respective irons with a hammer for final adjustment.

RIGHT

Clean this surface occasionally.

Fine for hardwood and smoothing plane. Increase for softwood and jack plane.

WRONG

Various faults with cap irons which require some filing to bed them tight on to the cutting iron.

SETTING JACK AND SMOOTHING PLANES

Releasing the iron.

Hit front of wood jack plane.

With fingers under sole and thumb pressing on iron, hit plane sharply with a hammer or mallet. Avoid unsightly hammer marks.

Hit back of wood smoothing plane.

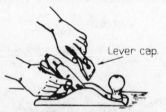

Lever cap.

Iron smoothing planes have depth and side adjustments. To set, lay plane on a flat surface and insert iron. Now tighten lever cap.

Inserting the iron.

Insert iron and grip with thumb. Sight along sole of plane on to a whitish surface. Put in wedge and tighten with a hammer.

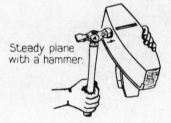

Steady plane with a hammer.

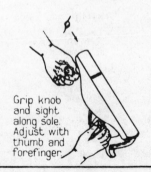

Grip knob and sight along sole. Adjust with thumb and forefinger.

TRYING PLANE AND IRON JOINTER

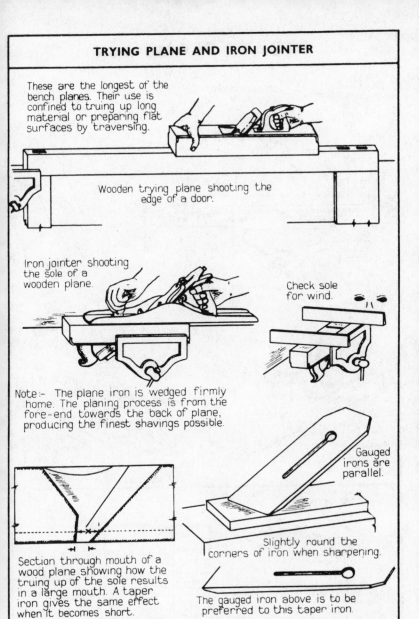

These are the longest of the bench planes. Their use is confined to truing up long material or preparing flat surfaces by traversing.

Wooden trying plane shooting the edge of a door.

Iron jointer shooting the sole of a wooden plane.

Check sole for wind.

Note:– The plane iron is wedged firmly home. The planing process is from the fore-end towards the back of plane, producing the finest shavings possible.

Gauged irons are parallel.

Slightly round the corners of iron when sharpening.

Section through mouth of a wood plane showing how the truing up of the sole results in a large mouth. A taper iron gives the same effect when it becomes short.

The gauged iron above is to be preferred to this taper iron.

REBATE PLANE IN USE

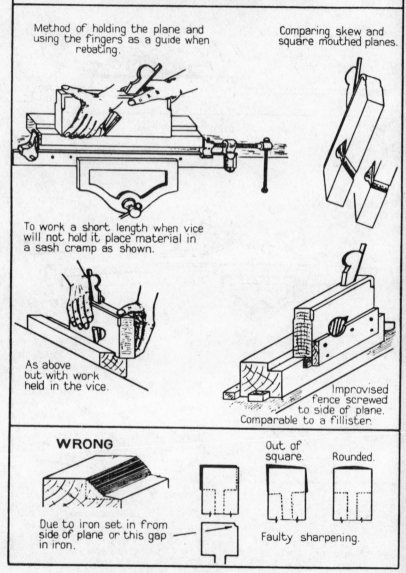

Method of holding the plane and using the fingers as a guide when rebating.

Comparing skew and square mouthed planes.

To work a short length when vice will not hold it place material in a sash cramp as shown.

As above but with work held in the vice.

Improvised fence screwed to side of plane. Comparable to a fillister.

WRONG

Due to iron set in from side of plane or this gap in iron.

Out of square.

Rounded.

Faulty sharpening.

SETTING **REBATE PLANE**

RIGHT	**WRONG**

It is possible to split the plane if hit here.

To remove the iron loosen wedge.

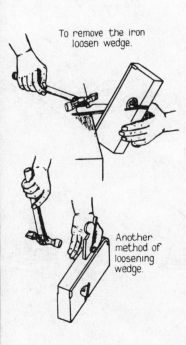

Another method of loosening wedge.

No support for wedge and it breaks.

Tap iron with hammer handle for any side adjustment.

Edge of iron damaged when hammer is used.

SHOULDER AND BULLNOSE PLANES

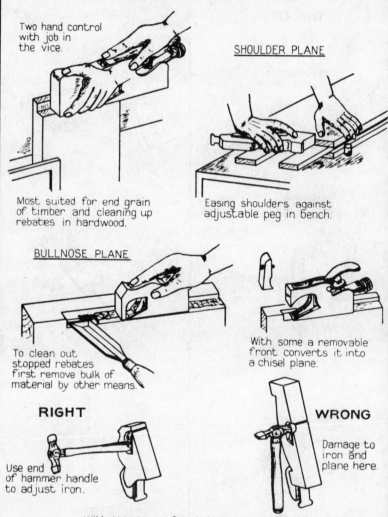

Two hand control with job in the vice.

SHOULDER PLANE

Most suited for end grain of timber and cleaning up rebates in hardwood.

Easing shoulders against adjustable peg in bench.

BULLNOSE PLANE

To clean out stopped rebates first remove bulk of material by other means.

With some a removable front converts it into a chisel plane.

RIGHT

WRONG

Use end of hammer handle to adjust iron.

Damage to iron and plane here.

With this type of metal plane, tap the wood wedge to remove the cutting iron. Never hit the plane with a hammer.

BADGER AND SIDE - REBATE PLANES

This plane is the same size as a jack plane. Used for cleaning out wide rebates similar to operation shown.

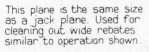
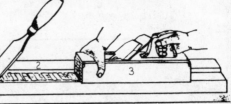

1. Plough groove. 2. Chop out waste.
3. Clean out rebate.

Comparing skew and square mouthed planes.

The square mouthed panel plane can be a converted jack plane. The fillet is removed for rebating purposes.

Straight edge

Known as an iron badger plane on account of its use as such. The manufacturers list it as a "Rabbet or Carriage makers plane".

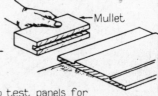

←Mullet

To test panels for thickness a mullet is used. This is a short end of material having a groove of the correct size.

SIDE REBATE PLANE

A single handed LEFT HAND plane is shown but double handed types are also available for widening grooves and housings or forming dovetailed housings.

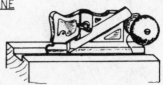

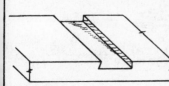

A pair of this type are required in order to operate right and left hand. Where grain tears up in one particular direction, or stopped grooves are encountered both hands are needed to deal with such conditions.

FILLISTERS

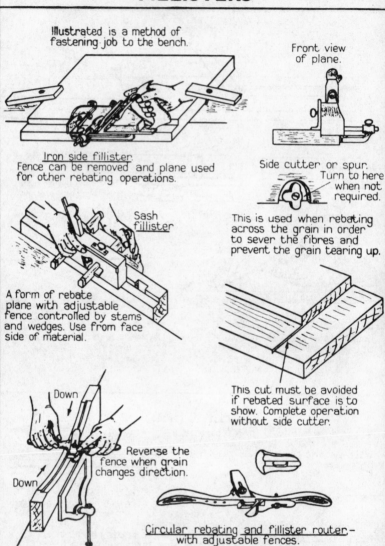

Illustrated is a method of fastening job to the bench.

Front view of plane.

Iron side fillister.
Fence can be removed and plane used for other rebating operations.

Side cutter or spur.
Turn to here when not required.

This is used when rebating across the grain in order to sever the fibres and prevent the grain tearing up.

Sash fillister

A form of rebate plane with adjustable fence controlled by stems and wedges. Use from face side of material.

This cut must be avoided if rebated surface is to show. Complete operation without side cutter.

Down

Down

Reverse the fence when grain changes direction.

Circular rebating and fillister router - with adjustable fences.

PLOUGH PLANE

This plane is used to form grooves in the direction of the grain.

Depth gauge adjustment

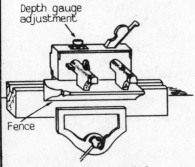

Fence

Plough irons are supplied in eight different sizes.

Hold the fence firmly to face of timber. Commence from the front and work gradually back.

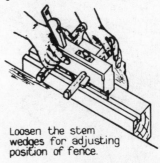

Loosen the stem wedges for adjusting position of fence.

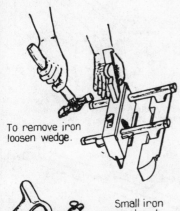

To remove iron loosen wedge.

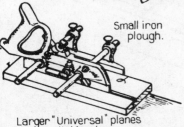

Small iron plough.

Larger "Universal" planes are available also.

WRONG

Plane will split if hit here continually.

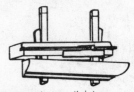

Fence not parallel to body of the plane, this causes it to bind in the groove being made.

37

MOULDING TOOLS

The term "stick" is used when forming mouldings. Standard sections of mouldings are obtainable in plane form.
To use and maintain these planes treat as for rebate plane.

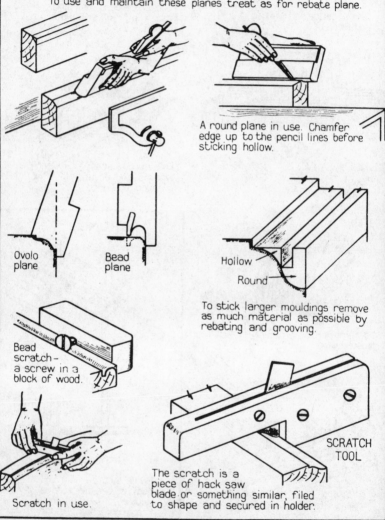

A round plane in use. Chamfer edge up to the pencil lines before sticking hollow.

Ovolo plane

Bead plane

Hollow

Round

To stick larger mouldings remove as much material as possible by rebating and grooving.

Bead scratch – a screw in a block of wood.

Scratch in use.

The scratch is a piece of hack saw blade or something similar, filed to shape and secured in holder.

SCRATCH TOOL

TOOTHING PLANE

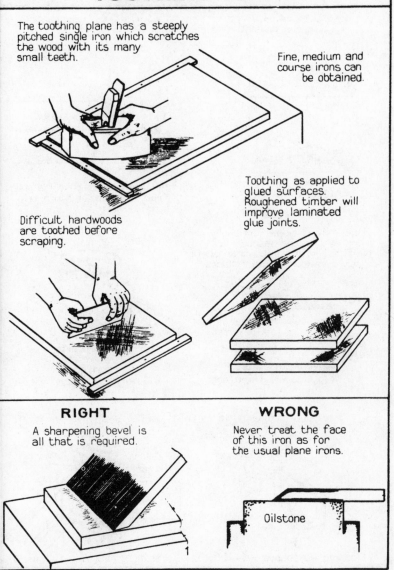

The toothing plane has a steeply pitched single iron which scratches the wood with its many small teeth.

Fine, medium and course irons can be obtained.

Difficult hardwoods are toothed before scraping.

Toothing as applied to glued surfaces. Roughened timber will improve laminated glue joints.

RIGHT

A sharpening bevel is all that is required.

WRONG

Never treat the face of this iron as for the usual plane irons.

Oilstone

BLOCK PLANE

A useful plane for light work.
It can be controlled easily with one hand.

Adjustable block plane.

Another model having an adjustable mouth.

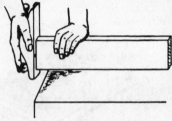

To plane end grain hold timber firmly over end of bench or stool.

Planes having single low angle irons rely on the sharpening bevel to perform in the manner a cap iron would in other planes.

RIGHT

Good cutting angle.

WRONG

An inefficient thick edge.

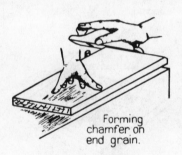

Forming chamfer on end grain.

Cleaning up shaped work.

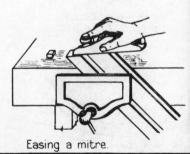

Easing a mitre.

COMPASS AND THUMB PLANES

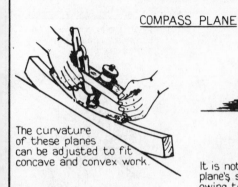

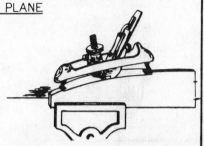

The curvature of these planes can be adjusted to fit concave and convex work.

It is not good policy to flex the plane's sole to a sharp curvature owing to the type of damage shown below. When in doubt clean up with a spokeshave. A smoothing plane could also do the above operation quite well.

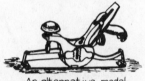

An alternative model. When a plane is not needed immediately, the sole should be returned to a flat position.

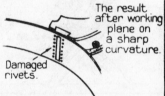

The result after working plane on a sharp curvature.

Damaged rivets.

THUMB PLANES

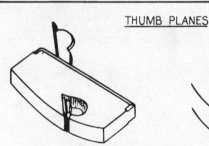

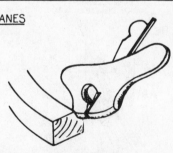

Two types are shown but there are many others from 16 to 38 mm wide, which are usually made to suit the operators particular requirements. They are of rebate or moulding section, having concave or convex faces to fit the curvature of the job.

ROUTERS

Adjustable iron router.
For accurate work and a clean finish.

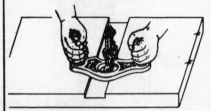

Wood router-"Old woman's tooth".
Plough irons are used to obtain a regular depth to grooves etc. with this tool.

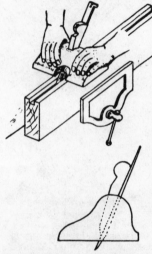

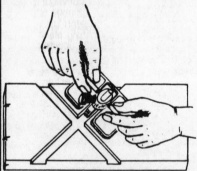

Small iron router-used for more delicate work.

Typical section of router. Due to the iron's steep angle a clean finish is difficult to obtain. A plough iron is often used as a cutter.

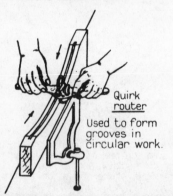

Quirk router

Used to form grooves in circular work.

Reverse the cutter when grain of timber changes direction.

Sides of cutter act as a gauge, the material being removed by the following chisel edge.

SPOKESHAVE

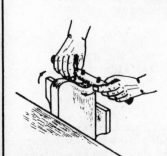

Shaping material in the vice. Work with the grain at all times. Do not plane into it. See arrows.

Cutter often becomes loose. Insert two round head screws to overcome this.

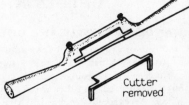

Cutter removed

Iron spokeshave - adjustable type.

Round face.   Flat face.

Cutter of an iron spokeshave will be easier sharpened if secured in a holder such as this.

Sharpen cutter of wood spokeshave in this manner

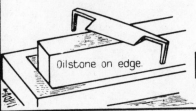

Oilstone on edge.

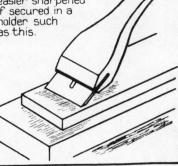

43

CHISELS AND GOUGES

HANDLING CHISELS AND GOUGES

THESE tools are no doubt the cause of the majority of accidents to the hands. They can be of a serious nature, but even minor cuts can be avoided when the golden rule of keeping both hands behind the cutting edge is observed. In other words, control the chisel or gouge with both hands. An exception to this is where a mallet is being used to strike the handle. The job itself must he held in a firm manner by some means.

Excessive pressure on a blunt tool will result in the grain of timber being torn out rather than pared away cleanly. Therefore keep the edges sharp and not too thick by the correct use of the oilstone and grindstone.

TYPES OF CHISELS

<u>Firmer chisel</u> for general work.

Firmer chisel with an octagonal handle. Does not roll on bench if position of dotted line is observed.

Clear of bench here.

<u>Registered firmer chisel</u> has an iron ferrule at striking end of handle. Suitable for carpentry work.

<u>Bevelled edge chisel</u> with oval carver type handle. Most suited for work of a precise nature.

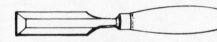

<u>Bevelled edge paring chisel</u>. Also firmer type. Blade much longer than other chisels.

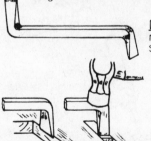

<u>Drawer lock chisel</u>. For chopping mortises etc. in confined positions, such as mortise for drawer lock- -see below.

Uses of the separate ends of the chisel.

MORTISE CHISELS

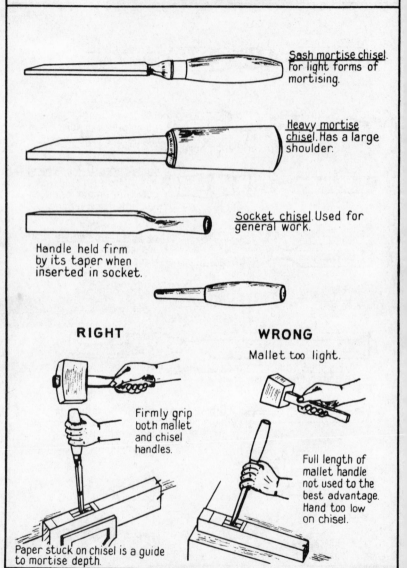

Sash mortise chisel. For light forms of mortising.

Heavy mortise chisel. Has a large shoulder.

Socket chisel. Used for general work.

Handle held firm by its taper when inserted in socket.

RIGHT

Firmly grip both mallet and chisel handles.

Paper stuck on chisel is a guide to mortise depth.

WRONG

Mallet too light.

Full length of mallet handle not used to the best advantage. Hand too low on chisel.

CARE OF CHISELS

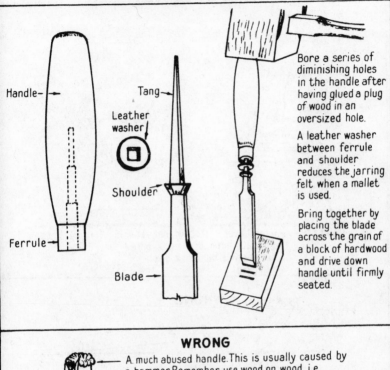

Handle—

Tang—

Leather washer—

Shoulder—

Blade—

Ferrule—

Bore a series of diminishing holes in the handle after having glued a plug of wood in an oversized hole.

A leather washer between ferrule and shoulder reduces the jarring felt when a mallet is used.

Bring together by placing the blade across the grain of a block of hardwood and drive down handle until firmly seated.

WRONG

A much abused handle. This is usually caused by a hammer. Remember, use wood on wood i.e. A mallet on chisel handles.

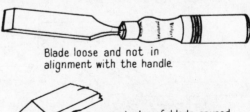

Blade loose and not in alignment with the handle.

Undersize hole for tang and a split handle results.

Damaged edge of blade caused by using it to scrape gritty surfaces. This never sharpens out.

47

SHARPENING CHISELS

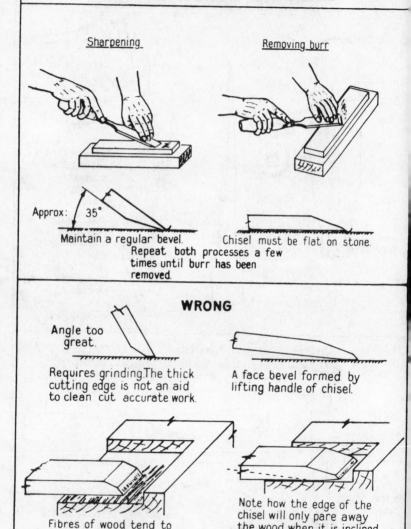

Sharpening

Removing burr

Approx: 35°

Maintain a regular bevel.

Chisel must be flat on stone.

Repeat both processes a few times until burr has been removed.

WRONG

Angle too great.

Requires grinding. The thick cutting edge is not an aid to clean cut accurate work.

A face bevel formed by lifting handle of chisel.

Fibres of wood tend to crush and therefore a ragged finish to work results.

Note how the edge of the chisel will only pare away the wood when it is inclined as shown by the dotted line.

CHISELS IN USE

Both hands behind the cutting edge at all times

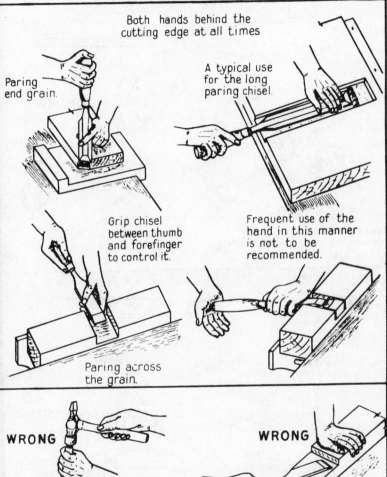

Paring end grain.

A typical use for the long paring chisel.

Grip chisel between thumb and forefinger to control it.

Frequent use of the hand in this manner is not to be recommended.

Paring across the grain.

WRONG

A mallet should be used.
Also chisel is too short.

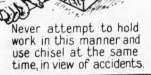

WRONG

Never attempt to hold work in this manner and use chisel at the same time, in view of accidents.

FIRMER AND SCRIBING GOUGES

<u>FIRMER GOUGE</u> – ground on convex face.

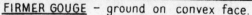

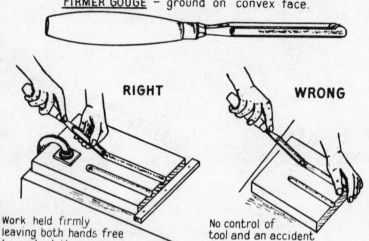

RIGHT

WRONG

Work held firmly
leaving both hands free
to control the gouge.

No control of
tool and an accident
is obvious.

<u>SCRIBING GOUGE</u> – ground on concave face.

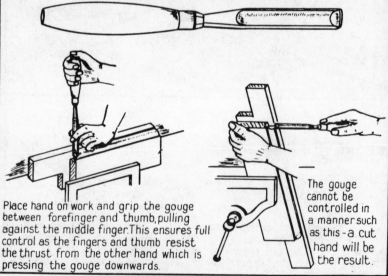

Place hand on work and grip the gouge
between forefinger and thumb, pulling
against the middle finger. This ensures full
control as the fingers and thumb resist
the thrust from the other hand which is
pressing the gouge downwards.

The gouge
cannot be
controlled in
a manner such
as this - a cut
hand will be
the result.

SHARPENING GOUGES

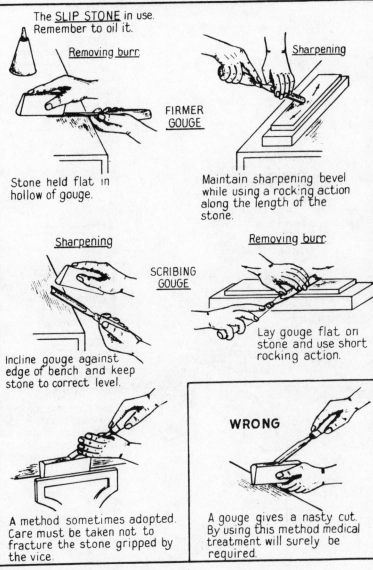

The <u>SLIP STONE</u> in use.
Remember to oil it.

<u>Removing burr.</u>

FIRMER GOUGE

Stone held flat in hollow of gouge.

<u>Sharpening</u>

Maintain sharpening bevel while using a rocking action along the length of the stone.

<u>Sharpening</u>

SCRIBING GOUGE

Incline gouge against edge of bench and keep stone to correct level.

<u>Removing burr.</u>

Lay gouge flat on stone and use short rocking action.

A method sometimes adopted. Care must be taken not to fracture the stone gripped by the vice.

WRONG

A gouge gives a nasty cut. By using this method medical treatment will surely be required.

MALLET

100-180mm mallet is a reasonable size.

A good sound ash or beechwood mallet is essential. The ideal end grain section is indicated.

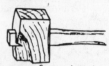

Keep away from heat. Here a shake may have developed and a piece splits off on impact. Periodical oiling will help to preserve the wood.

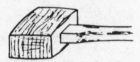

Round off the surfaces of the two large faces slightly. This prevents damage to framing when knocking it together.

The head should be slightly tapered. This is excessive and makes it difficult to hit a chisel squarely.

WRONG

The end grain of a mallet is for using on chisel handles, not framing.

Damaged edges to the work will be the result.

WRONG

Use the end grain. The face will quickly break up if used in this manner. The grain of the head in this case is wrong also.

BORING TOOLS

BRACE AND BITS

A BRACE of inferior quality is not a good investment when one considers the number of revolutions the moving parts have to make. The ratchet brace with not too small a sweep is the best proposition, the greater circumference making work easier when boring large holes. The provision of the ratchet becomes an asset when boring in awkward corners, or when making a full turn of the brace becomes laborious.

The hand drill (wheel brace) will prove of great value when small counter-sunk holes and the like are required, the morse pattern drill being used for this purpose.

Protect twist bits from damage by placing them separately in a 'hold-all' before rolling it up.

TYPES OF BITS

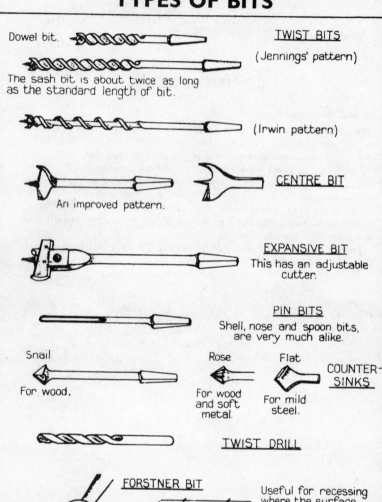

Dowel bit.

TWIST BITS

(Jennings' pattern)

The sash bit is about twice as long as the standard length of bit.

(Irwin pattern)

CENTRE BIT

An improved pattern.

EXPANSIVE BIT

This has an adjustable cutter.

PIN BITS

Shell, nose and spoon bits, are very much alike.

Snail

For wood.

Rose

For wood and soft metal.

Flat

For mild steel.

COUNTER-SINKS

TWIST DRILL

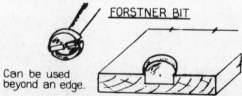

FORSTNER BIT

Can be used beyond an edge.

Useful for recessing where the surface must be free of the centre point marks which would be left by other types of bit.

RATCHET BRACE

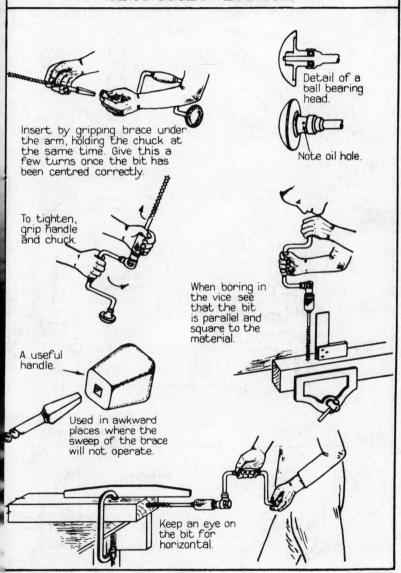

Insert by gripping brace under the arm, holding the chuck at the same time. Give this a few turns once the bit has been centred correctly.

Detail of a ball bearing head.

Note oil hole.

To tighten, grip handle and chuck.

When boring in the vice see that the bit is parallel and square to the material.

A useful handle.

Used in awkward places where the sweep of the brace will not operate.

Keep an eye on the bit for horizontal.

BORING OPERATIONS

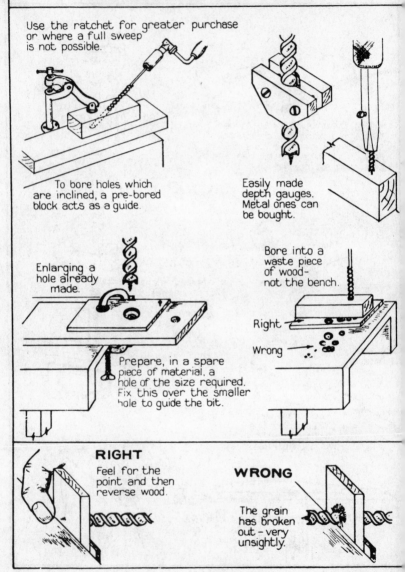

Use the ratchet for greater purchase or where a full sweep is not possible.

To bore holes which are inclined, a pre-bored block acts as a guide.

Easily made depth gauges. Metal ones can be bought.

Enlarging a hole already made.

Prepare, in a spare piece of material, a hole of the size required. Fix this over the smaller hole to guide the bit.

Bore into a waste piece of wood - not the bench.

Right

Wrong

RIGHT

Feel for the point and then reverse wood.

WRONG

The grain has broken out - very unsightly.

HAND DRILL

Hand drills are used extensively to drill for the shank of screws, pilot holes and any drilling or countersinking of a light nature.

Sharpening drills. Each cutting lip in its turn is held horizontally, the drill being inclined at approximately 60° to the stone.

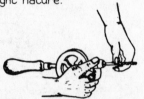

Place drill in jaws and grip handle to tighten chuck.

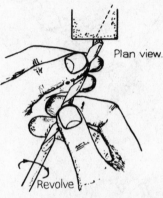

Plan view.

Revolve

Pressure downwards can be exercised if the thumb is placed over the end of the hand grip.

Drilling vertically.

Held firmly.

Result when boring insecure material.

Side view.

Lip horizontal.

Revolve

The drill is also inclined to the horizontal, the angle being altered to that of the dotted line as the drill is revolved.

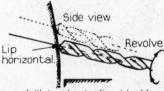

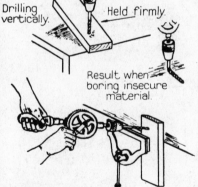

With horizontal drilling ensure that the tool is supported correctly otherwise the drill will break.

Clearance

Cutting edge

RIGHT
Clearance behind cutting edge.

WRONG
Cutting edge has no clearance.

SHARPENING BITS

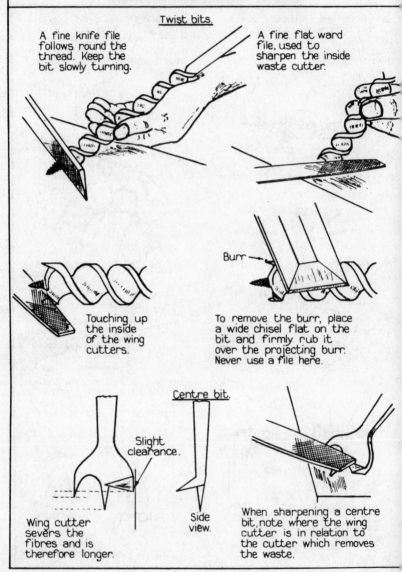

Twist bits.

A fine knife file follows round the thread. Keep the bit slowly turning.

A fine flat ward file, used to sharpen the inside waste cutter.

Touching up the inside of the wing cutters.

Burr

To remove the burr, place a wide chisel flat on the bit and firmly rub it over the projecting burr. Never use a file here.

Centre bit.

Slight clearance.

Wing cutter severs the fibres and is therefore longer.

Side view.

When sharpening a centre bit, note where the wing cutter is in relation to the cutter which removes the waste.

SELECTING AND PREPARING TIMBER

THE nature of timber is such that everybody, at one time or another, has attempted to make something with it. It is easy to work and pieces are readily joined together by various means.

Timber is classified as softwood or hardwood, but this does not always mean that their working qualities will be soft or hard. It is purely a means of grouping trees with needle-like leaves and bearing cones (coniferous) under the heading of softwood, and the broad-leaf tree which loses its leaves annually (deciduous) under hardwoods. There are a few exceptions to this general division of trees but they are not important.

In all trees there is a band of wood nearest the bark known as sapwood. This is immature wood compared with the remainder which is heartwood. Both heart and sapwood are used, but a fact not to be overlooked is that the sapwood is prone to decay through fungal or insect attack, unless it has been suitably preserved.

The structure of timber comprises numerous minute cells held together by a cellulose substance. They are interconnected by means of pits which convey sap moisture. A large amount of moisture has to be extracted before the timber can be used and this process is known as seasoning. It is because of the cellular nature of timber that it has the ability to absorb moisture under wet conditions, causing it to swell, and then, of course, the reverse holds good if warmer conditions are met with, when shrinkage takes place. It is this movement of solid timber which has to be taken care of by constructional details, such as an allowance in a groove for the movement of a panel.

By using plywood, laminated boards, hardboard and chipboard such difficulties are overcome because there is no movement in such materials. This makes them ideally suited for work involving large areas, where otherwise a number of narrow boards would have to be jointed together.

The commonly known yellow or red deal is the European redwood, a fir tree, and most popular of the softwoods for work of a painted or general constructional nature. Hardwoods of mahogany and walnut are usually selected for their decorative qualities, whilst oak can be used for almost all types of work in wood. Selected quarter-sawn oak is more expensive because of its well-known silver grain figure, but for economy it is usual to obtain this effect in veneer form for panels and the like.

When selecting timber for a job, bear in mind any defects, knots and shakes etc., which may interfere with the finished appearance. Also it must not be overlooked that the usual sizes obtainable are nominal sawn sizes and an allowance has to be made for planing up, whether it be by hand or machine. It is necessary to allow 3 mm less in both width and thickness and even more if the wood is fairly long or twisted. Therefore design a job around, for example, a 72 mm × 47 mm, this being originally a 75 mm × 50 mm piece of material.

SOLID AND LAMINATED BOARDS

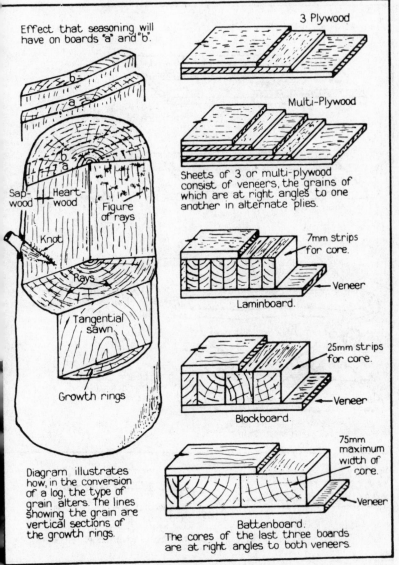

Effect that seasoning will have on boards "a" and "b".

Sap-wood — Heart-wood

Figure of rays

Knot

Rays

Tangential sawn

Growth rings

Diagram illustrates how, in the conversion of a log, the type of grain alters. The lines showing the grain are vertical sections of the growth rings.

3 Plywood

Multi-Plywood

Sheets of 3 or multi-plywood consist of veneers, the grains of which are at right angles to one another in alternate plies.

7mm strips for core.

Veneer

Laminboard.

25mm strips for core.

Veneer

Blockboard.

75mm maximum width of core.

Veneer

Battenboard.
The cores of the last three boards are at right angles to both veneers.

MARKING OUT BOARDS FOR SAWN SIZES

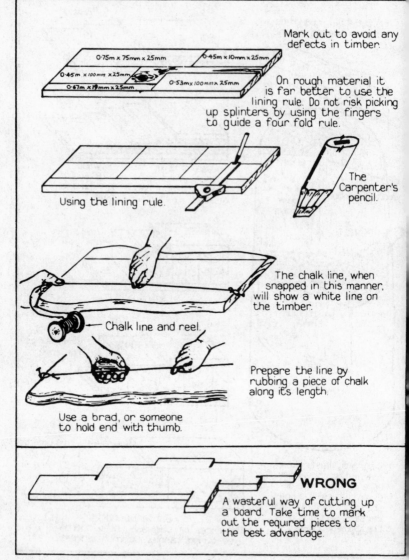

Mark out to avoid any defects in timber.

0·75m x 75mm x 25mm
0·45m x 10mm x 25mm
0·45m x 100mm x 25mm
0·67m x 19mm x 25mm
0·53m x 100mm x 25mm

On rough material it is far better to use the lining rule. Do not risk picking up splinters by using the fingers to guide a four fold rule.

Using the lining rule.

The Carpenter's pencil.

The chalk line, when snapped in this manner, will show a white line on the timber.

Chalk line and reel.

Prepare the line by rubbing a piece of chalk along its length.

Use a brad, or someone to hold end with thumb.

WRONG

A wasteful way of cutting up a board. Take time to mark out the required pieces to the best advantage.

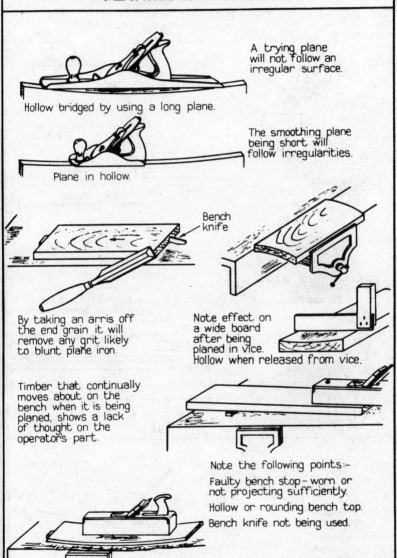

A trying plane will not follow an irregular surface.

Hollow bridged by using a long plane.

The smoothing plane being short will follow irregularities.

Plane in hollow.

Bench knife

By taking an arris off the end grain it will remove any grit likely to blunt plane iron.

Note effect on a wide board after being planed in vice.
Hollow when released from vice.

Timber that continually moves about on the bench when it is being planed, shows a lack of thought on the operator's part.

Note the following points :-

Faulty bench stop - worn or not projecting sufficiently.

Hollow or rounding bench top.

Bench knife not being used.

FACE SIDE PREPARATION

To prepare the face side correctly is essential.

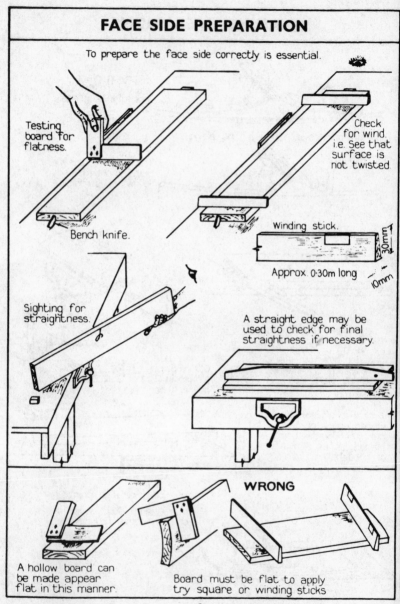

Testing board for flatness.

Bench knife.

Check for wind. i.e. See that surface is not twisted.

Winding stick.

30mm

10mm

Approx. 0·30m long

Sighting for straightness.

A straight edge may be used to check for final straightness if necessary.

WRONG

A hollow board can be made appear flat in this manner.

Board must be flat to apply try square or winding sticks

64

FACE EDGE AND GAUGING TO SIZE

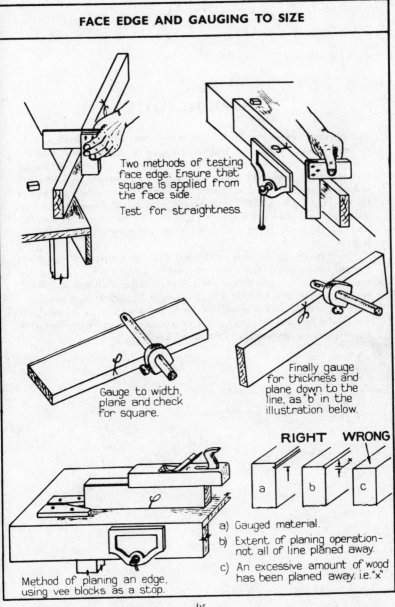

Two methods of testing face edge. Ensure that square is applied from the face side.

Test for straightness.

Gauge to width, plane and check for square.

Finally gauge for thickness and plane down to the line, as "b" in the illustration below.

RIGHT **WRONG**

a) Gauged material.

b) Extent of planing operation— not all of line planed away.

c) An excessive amount of wood has been planed away. i.e."x"

Method of planing an edge, using vee blocks as a stop.

MARKING OUT

THE operation of putting lines on the wood is not often carried out in the correct manner. A little thought given to similar dimensions and operations will save time and trouble. The practice of completely finishing off, one at a time, a number of identical joints must be avoided. This will only be possible if the marking of the whole job is carried out as one operation. That is, once the sight, mortise and shoulder lines are marked, gauge and cut lines will follow. All this must be done from the face side and edge as it will prevent a lot of unleasant surprises during fitting up later on.

Attention should be paid to the fact that not all pairs of things are reversible any more than a pair of shoes is. Make a point of 'handing' door stiles; for instance, when the top and bottom rails are of different widths; and in fact, use this practice of right and left hand always.

A warning about cut lines; use them only where a saw or chisel will eventually be used. The purpose of such a line is to sever the fibres and leave a clean edge once the waste wood has been cut away.

RULES FOR MEASURING AND LINING

Im four fold boxwood rule is the most popular as it goes easily in a pocket. Ensure it is marked for both metric and Imperial measurements.

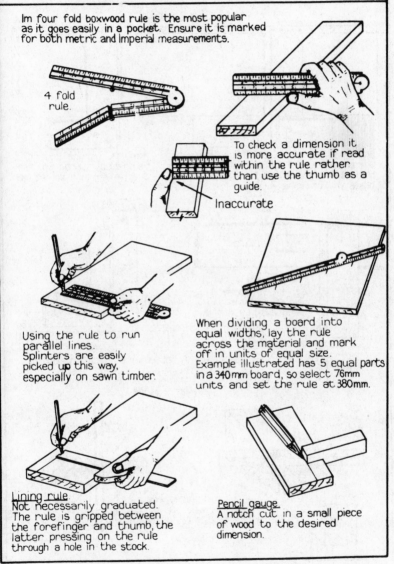

4 fold rule.

To check a dimension it is more accurate if read within the rule rather than use the thumb as a guide.

Inaccurate

Using the rule to run parallel lines. Splinters are easily picked up this way, especially on sawn timber.

When dividing a board into equal widths, lay the rule across the material and mark off in units of equal size. Example illustrated has 5 equal parts in a 340mm board, so select 76mm units and set the rule at 380mm.

Lining rule.
Not necessarily graduated. The rule is gripped between the forefinger and thumb, the latter pressing on the rule through a hole in the stock.

Pencil gauge.
A notch cut in a small piece of wood to the desired dimension.

SQUARES

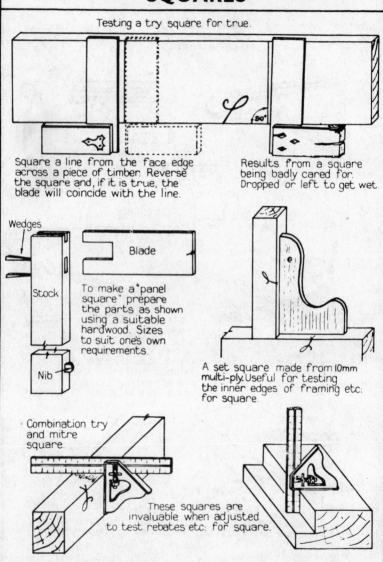

Testing a try square for true.

Square a line from the face edge across a piece of timber. Reverse the square and, if it is true, the blade will coincide with the line.

Results from a square being badly cared for. Dropped or left to get wet.

Wedges

Stock

Nib

Blade

To make a "panel square" prepare the parts as shown using a suitable hardwood. Sizes to suit one's own requirements.

A set square made from 10mm multi-ply. Useful for testing the inner edges of framing etc. for square.

Combination try and mitre square.

These squares are invaluable when adjusted to test rebates etc. for square.

BEVEL AND TRY MITRE

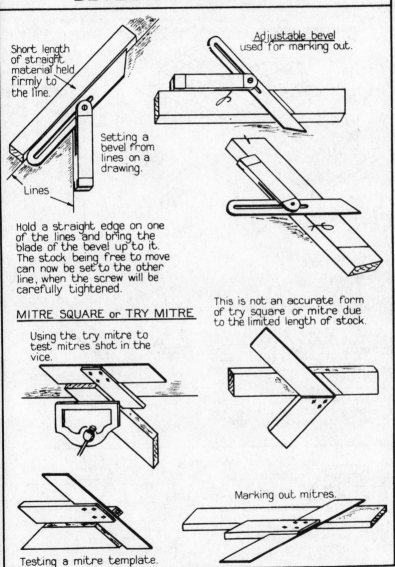

Short length of straight material held firmly to the line.

Setting a bevel from lines on a drawing.

Lines

Adjustable bevel used for marking out.

Hold a straight edge on one of the lines and bring the blade of the bevel up to it. The stock being free to move can now be set to the other line, when the screw will be carefully tightened.

MITRE SQUARE or TRY MITRE

This is not an accurate form of try square or mitre due to the limited length of stock.

Using the try mitre to test mitres shot in the vice.

Marking out mitres.

Testing a mitre template.

MARKING LINES ON TIMBER

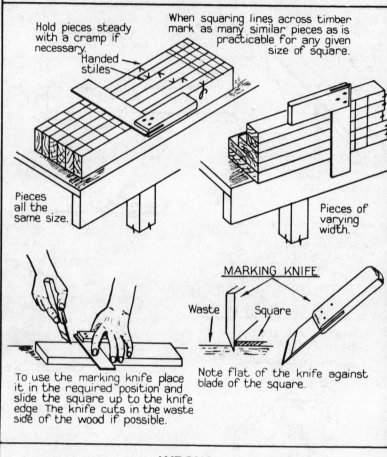

Hold pieces steady with a cramp if necessary.

Handed stiles

When squaring lines across timber mark as many similar pieces as is practicable for any given size of square.

Pieces all the same size.

Pieces of varying width.

MARKING KNIFE

Waste Square

To use the marking knife place it in the required position and slide the square up to the knife edge The knife cuts in the waste side of the wood if possible.

Note flat of the knife against blade of the square.

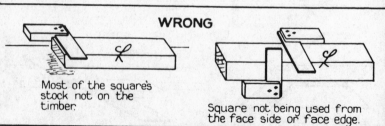

WRONG

Most of the square's stock not on the timber.

Square not being used from the face side or face edge.

MARKING GAUGE

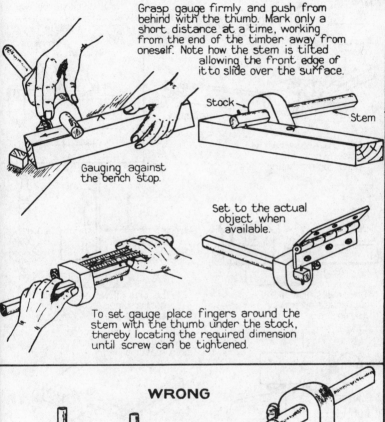

Grasp gauge firmly and push from behind with the thumb. Mark only a short distance at a time, working from the end of the timber away from oneself. Note how the stem is tilted allowing the front edge of it to slide over the surface.

Stock

Stem

Gauging against the bench stop.

Set to the actual object when available.

To set gauge place fingers around the stem with the thumb under the stock, thereby locating the required dimension until screw can be tightened.

WRONG

Two types of spur to be avoided.

There is no control when held in this manner. The spur will leave unsightly scratches.

MORTISE AND CUTTING GAUGES

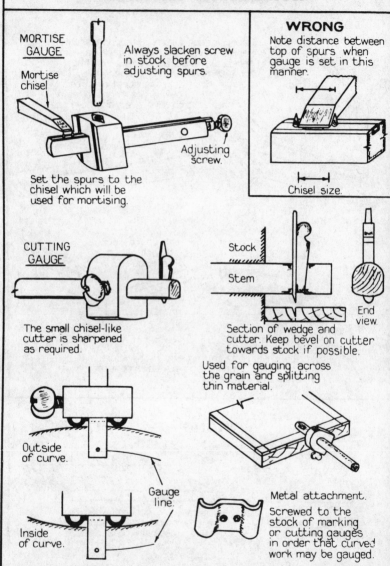

MORTISE GAUGE

Mortise chisel

Always slacken screw in stock before adjusting spurs.

Adjusting screw.

Set the spurs to the chisel which will be used for mortising.

WRONG

Note distance between top of spurs when gauge is set in this manner.

Chisel size.

CUTTING GAUGE

The small chisel-like cutter is sharpened as required.

Stock

Stem

End view.

Section of wedge and cutter. Keep bevel on cutter towards stock if possible.

Used for gauging across the grain and splitting thin material.

Outside of curve.

Inside of curve.

Gauge line.

Metal attachment.

Screwed to the stock of marking or cutting gauges in order that curved work may be gauged.

DIVIDERS AND TRAMMELS

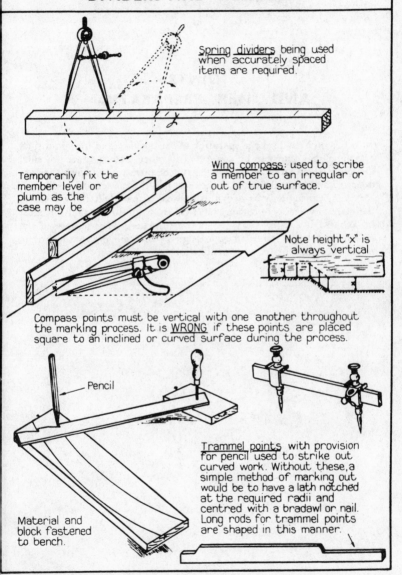

Spring dividers being used when accurately spaced items are required.

Temporarily fix the member level or plumb as the case may be

Wing compass: used to scribe a member to an irregular or out of true surface.

Note height "x" is always vertical

Compass points must be vertical with one another throughout the marking process. It is WRONG if these points are placed square to an inclined or curved surface during the process.

Pencil

Material and block fastened to bench.

Trammel points with provision for pencil used to strike out curved work. Without these, a simple method of marking out would be to have a lath notched at the required radii and centred with a bradawl or nail. Long rods for trammel points are shaped in this manner.

JOINTS
AND THEIR PREPARATION

THERE is no limit to the preparation of various pieces of timber in such a manner that they can be connected together, but, as a general rule, the joints which are illustrated will serve the purposes for which they are designed and are sufficient to cover most jobs that are encountered.

A joint can be only as strong as its weakest part will allow it to be, therefore any excessive cutting will weaken it still further and this must be avoided if a satisfactory job is contemplated. The mastery of the mortise and tenon joint will go a long way to achieving that feeling of having accomplished a workmanlike job.

MORTISE AND TENON

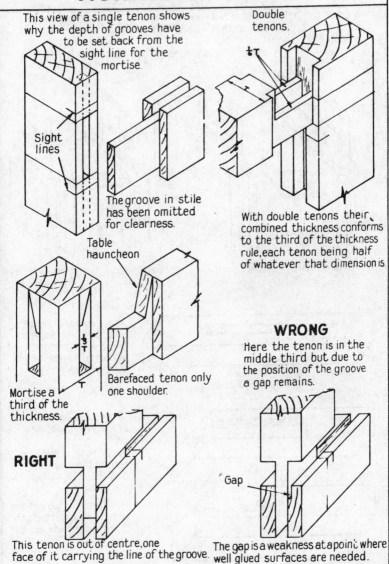

This view of a single tenon shows why the depth of grooves have to be set back from the sight line for the mortise.

Sight lines

The groove in stile has been omitted for clearness.

Double tenons.

⅓T

With double tenons their combined thickness conforms to the third of the thickness rule, each tenon being half of whatever that dimension is.

Table hauncheon

⅓T

T

Mortise a third of the thickness.

Barefaced tenon only one shoulder.

WRONG

Here the tenon is in the middle third but due to the position of the groove a gap remains.

RIGHT

This tenon is out of centre, one face of it carrying the line of the groove.

Gap

The gap is a weakness at a point where well glued surfaces are needed.

PROPORTIONS OF TENON

A guide to the thickness of a tenon is that its mortise will be a third of the thickness of that material. The width of a tenon will be not more than five times its thickness. For variations concerning hauncheons see diagrams.

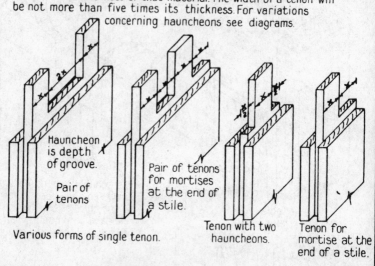

Hauncheon is depth of groove.

Pair of tenons

Various forms of single tenon.

Pair of tenons for mortises at the end of a stile.

Tenon with two hauncheons.

Tenon for mortise at the end of a stile.

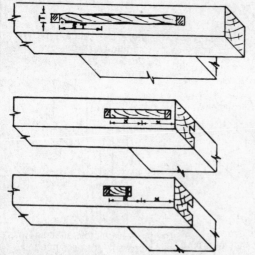

The excessive width will cause the tenon to buckle when wedged. A pair of tenons would be the answer.

A tenon is only as strong as its weakest part.
Here there is nothing behind the end wedge and the stile will split.

This tenon is too narrow to have much strength. It will break off at its root.

CUTTING FLANKS OF TENON

A half rip, or hand saw, is the most efficient tool for work of this nature.

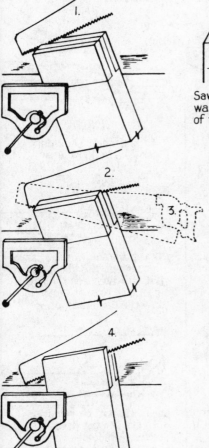

RIGHT

Saw cut in waste side of tenon.

WRONG

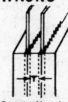

Gauge line is not the centre of cut.

Note thickness "T"

Sequence of sawing operations.

Position 1.
Commence by sawing the edge of the timber away from oneself.

Position 2.
Work saw across end grain. It is easier to follow one gauge line at a time.

Position 3.
Now follow the gauge line down the nearest edge but keep the toe of the saw just in the timber all the time.

Position 4.
Having sawn down the remaining flank of the tenon, turn work round in the vice, enter saw in the cut already made and continue sawing to the shoulder line but not beyond it.

CUTTING SHOULDERS

RIGHT

Commence to saw on the edge away from oneself lowering the heel as the cut deepens.

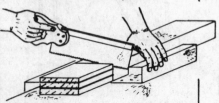

Note grooves and mouldings etc. must be already formed if required.

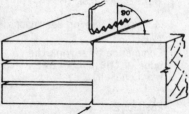

Marking knife cut line. Keep the saw to the waste side of this line and square to the surface.

Shallow saw cut.

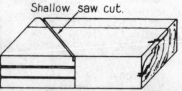

Showing a partly cut shoulder, necessary where a wide moulding is to be stuck. It can now be formed without losing most of the shoulder line.

WRONG

Job not securely held. Do not attempt to start saw flat on the timber.

An undercut shoulder shows a lack of saw control.

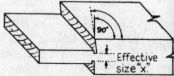

Do not oversaw. This is a common fault when the cheek does not fall away readily. The effective size of tenon is only the dimension of "x".

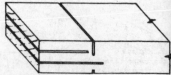

Cheek cannot be removed when the saw cut does not reach the shoulder line. An over-sawn tenon will show as an unsightly saw cut on the edge of a finished job.

MORTISING

RIGHT

Bevel of chisel faces towards partly formed mortise.

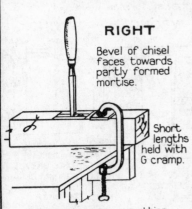

Short lengths held with G cramp.

Place mortise over something firm, such as the leg of a bench.

Attempt to have splayed mortises held in a vertical position as below.

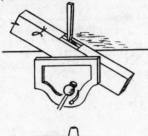

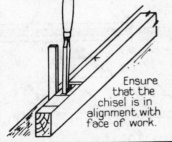

Ensure that the chisel is in alignment with face of work.

WRONG

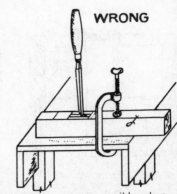

A solid blow is not possible when mortising in this position. The G cramp is a hinderence and will also damage the timber. Bevel on chisel should face mortise already chopped out.

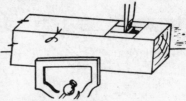

Timber too large to hold in a vice and the mortise is not central over it.

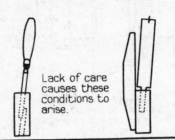

Lack of care causes these conditions to arise.

WEDGED JOINTS

Mortise and tenon joint cut away to show wedges.

RIGHT **WRONG** **WRONG**

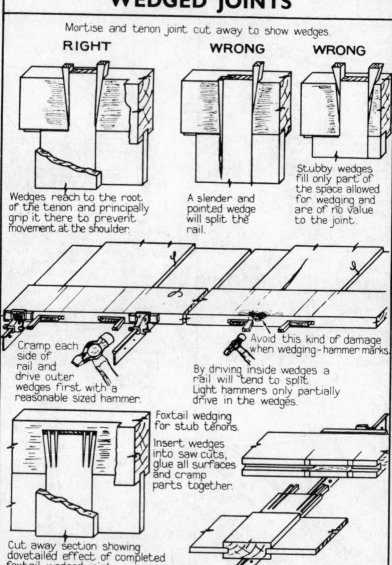

Wedges reach to the root of the tenon and principally grip it there to prevent movement at the shoulder.

A slender and pointed wedge will split the rail.

Stubby wedges fill only part of the space allowed for wedging and are of no value to the joint.

Cramp each side of rail and drive outer wedges first with a reasonable sized hammer.

Avoid this kind of damage when wedging—hammer marks.

By driving inside wedges a rail will tend to split. Light hammers only partially drive in the wedges.

Foxtail wedging for stub tenons.

Insert wedges into saw cuts, glue all surfaces and cramp parts together.

Cut away section showing dovetailed effect of completed foxtail-wedged joint.

DRAWBORING

This operation, in conjunction with the mortise and tenon is used on fairly large members. Gates and other external jobs are examples.

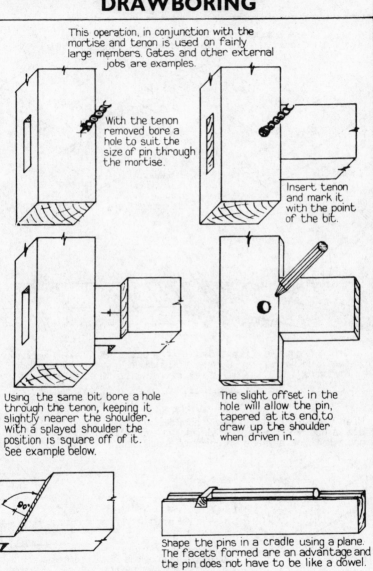

With the tenon removed bore a hole to suit the size of pin through the mortise.

Insert tenon and mark it with the point of the bit.

Using the same bit bore a hole through the tenon, keeping it slightly nearer the shoulder. With a splayed shoulder the position is square off of it. See example below.

The slight offset in the hole will allow the pin, tapered at its end, to draw up the shoulder when driven in.

Shape the pins in a cradle using a plane. The facets formed are an advantage and the pin does not have to be like a dowel.

HALVING JOINT

A popular joint. Often used instead of the mortise and tenon but lacking in its strength.

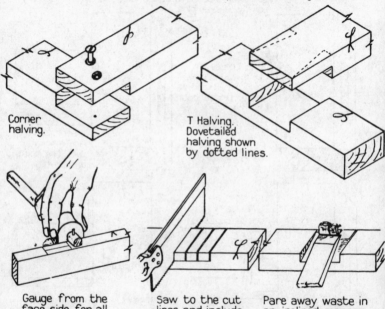

Corner halving.

T Halving. Dovetailed halving shown by dotted lines.

Gauge from the face side for all members.

Saw to the cut lines and include a few in the waste.

Pare away waste in an inclined manner. Reverse job and clean out the remainder.

WRONG

Over sawing results in weakness, see "x". Job is not flush because face marks are not consistent, and are on opposite sides.

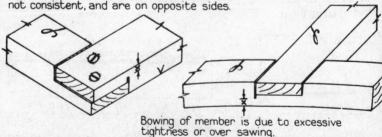

Bowing of member is due to excessive tightness or over sawing.

BRIDLE JOINT

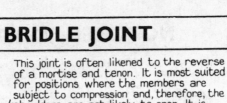

This joint is often likened to the reverse of a mortise and tenon. It is most suited for positions where the members are subject to compression and, therefore, the shoulders are not likely to open. It is designed to prevent lateral movement.

Bisect angle

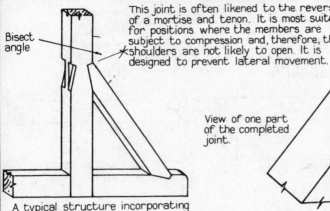

View of one part of the completed joint.

A typical structure incorporating bridle joints.

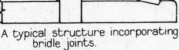

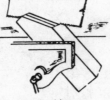

1. Shape abutting end and gauge to approx: a third of the thickness of the material.

2. Saw to the gauge lines.

3. Chisel out the centre waste.

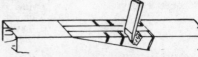

4. Make several inclined saw cuts between the lines, most of the waste being then chopped out with a chisel.

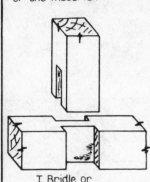

T. Bridle or forked joint.

5. Pare waste away after the majority of it has been removed as above.

NOTCHED JOINTS

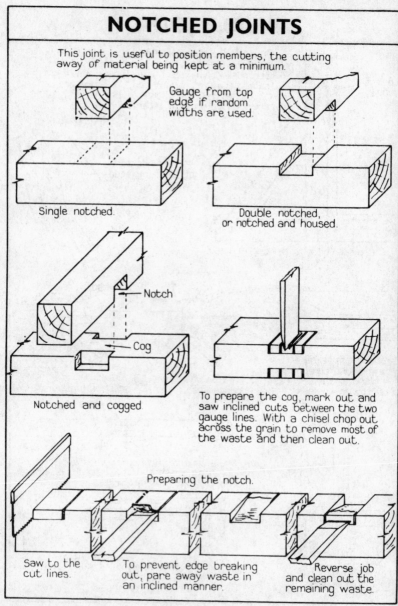

This joint is useful to position members, the cutting away of material being kept at a minimum.

Gauge from top edge if random widths are used.

Single notched.

Double notched, or notched and housed.

Notch

Cog

Notched and cogged.

To prepare the cog, mark out and saw inclined cuts between the two gauge lines. With a chisel chop out across the grain to remove most of the waste and then clean out.

Preparing the notch.

Saw to the cut lines.

To prevent edge breaking out, pare away waste in an inclined manner.

Reverse job and clean out the remaining waste.

HOUSED JOINT

This joint is used to connect shelves
to the standards and divisions of fittings.

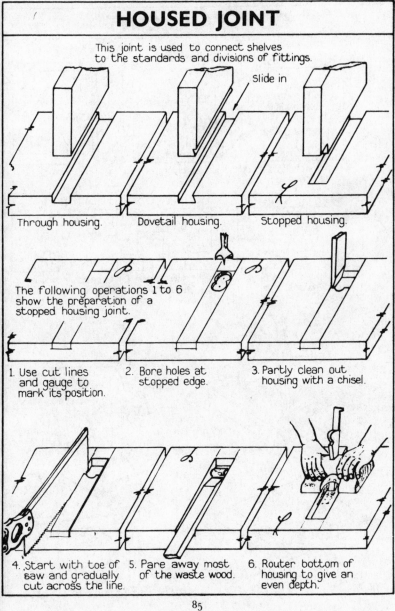

Slide in

Through housing.

Dovetail housing.

Stopped housing.

The following operations 1 to 6
show the preparation of a
stopped housing joint.

1. Use cut lines
   and gauge to
   mark its position.

2. Bore holes at
   stopped edge.

3. Partly clean out
   housing with a chisel.

4. Start with toe of
   saw and gradually
   cut across the line.

5. Pare away most
   of the waste wood.

6. Router bottom of
   housing to give an
   even depth.

DOVETAIL JOINT

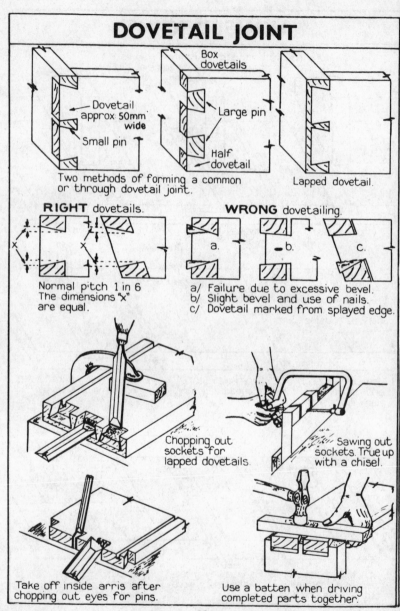

Dovetail approx 50mm wide

Small pin

Two methods of forming a common or through dovetail joint.

Box dovetails

Large pin

Half dovetail

Lapped dovetail.

RIGHT dovetails.

Normal pitch 1 in 6
The dimensions "x" are equal.

WRONG dovetailing.

a.   b.   c.

a/ Failure due to excessive bevel.
b/ Slight bevel and use of nails.
c/ Dovetail marked from splayed edge.

Chopping out sockets for lapped dovetails.

Sawing out sockets. True up with a chisel.

Take off inside arris after chopping out eyes for pins.

Use a batten when driving completed parts together.

DRAWER DOVETAILING

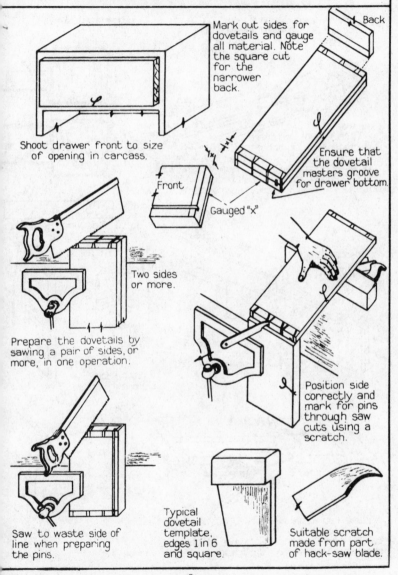

Shoot drawer front to size of opening in carcass.

Mark out sides for dovetails and gauge all material. Note the square cut for the narrower back.

Back

Front

Gauged "x"

Ensure that the dovetail masters groove for drawer bottom.

Two sides or more.

Prepare the dovetails by sawing a pair of sides, or more, in one operation.

Position side correctly and mark for pins through saw cuts using a scratch.

Saw to waste side of line when preparing the pins.

Typical dovetail template, edges 1 in 6 and square.

Suitable scratch made from part of hack-saw blade.

SHOOTING EDGE-JOINTS

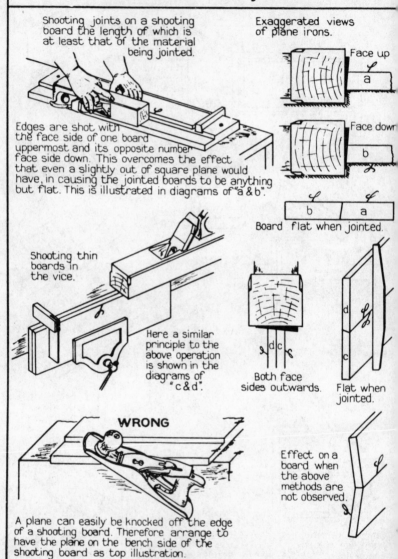

Shooting joints on a shooting board the length of which is at least that of the material being jointed.

Exaggerated views of plane irons.

Face up

a

Edges are shot with the face side of one board uppermost and its opposite number face side down. This overcomes the effect that even a slightly out of square plane would have, in causing the jointed boards to be anything but flat. This is illustrated in diagrams of "a & b".

Face down

b

b | a

Board flat when jointed.

Shooting thin boards in the vice.

Here a similar principle to the above operation is shown in the diagrams of "c & d".

Both face sides outwards.

d

c

Flat when jointed.

WRONG

Effect on a board when the above methods are not observed.

A plane can easily be knocked off the edge of a shooting board. Therefore arrange to have the plane on the bench side of the shooting board as top illustration.

EDGE JOINTING

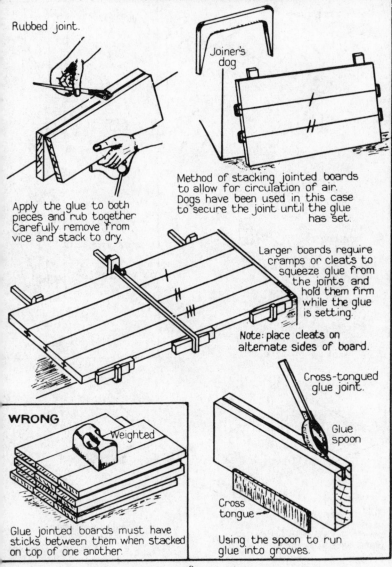

Rubbed joint.

Apply the glue to both pieces and rub together Carefully remove from vice and stack to dry.

Joiner's dog

Method of stacking jointed boards to allow for circulation of air. Dogs have been used in this case to secure the joint until the glue has set.

Larger boards require cramps or cleats to squeeze glue from the joints and hold them firm while the glue is setting.

Note: place cleats on alternate sides of board.

Cross-tongued glue joint.

Glue spoon

Cross tongue

WRONG

Weighted

Glue jointed boards must have sticks between them when stacked on top of one another.

Using the spoon to run glue into grooves.

DOWELLED JOINT

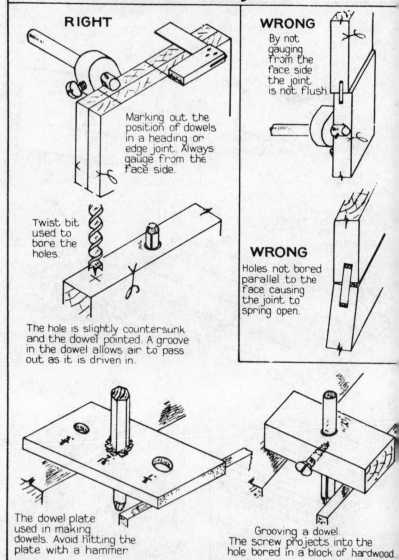

RIGHT

Marking out the position of dowels in a heading or edge joint. Always gauge from the face side.

Twist bit used to bore the holes.

The hole is slightly countersunk and the dowel pointed. A groove in the dowel allows air to pass out as it is driven in.

WRONG

By not gauging from the face side the joint is not flush.

WRONG

Holes not bored parallel to the face causing the joint to spring open.

The dowel plate used in making dowels. Avoid hitting the plate with a hammer

Grooving a dowel. The screw projects into the hole bored in a block of hardwood.

SCRIBED JOINTS

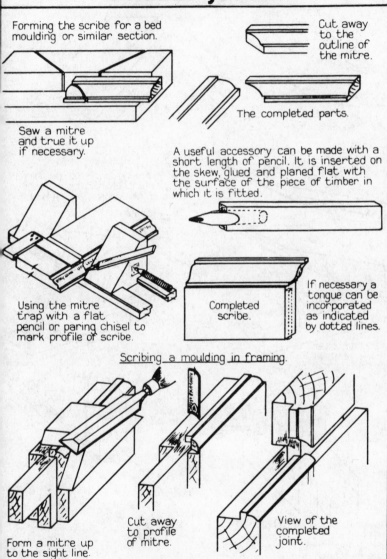

Forming the scribe for a bed moulding or similar section.

Saw a mitre and true it up if necessary.

Cut away to the outline of the mitre.

The completed parts.

A useful accessory can be made with a short length of pencil. It is inserted on the skew, glued and planed flat with the surface of the piece of timber in which it is fitted.

Using the mitre trap with a flat pencil or paring chisel to mark profile or scribe.

Completed scribe.

If necessary a tongue can be incorporated as indicated by dotted lines.

Scribing a moulding in framing.

Form a mitre up to the sight line.

Cut away to profile of mitre.

View of the completed joint.

MITRED JOINTS

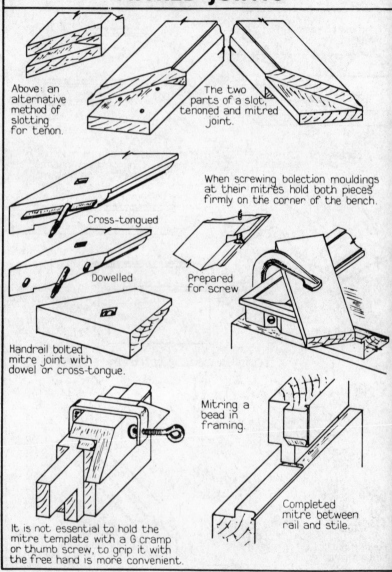

Above: an alternative method of slotting for tenon.

The two parts of a slot, tenoned and mitred joint.

Cross-tongued

Dowelled

When screwing bolection mouldings at their mitres hold both pieces firmly on the corner of the bench.

Prepared for screw

Handrail bolted mitre joint with dowel or cross-tongue.

It is not essential to hold the mitre template with a G cramp or thumb screw, to grip it with the free hand is more convenient.

Mitring a bead in framing.

Completed mitre between rail and stile.

MITRING MOULDINGS

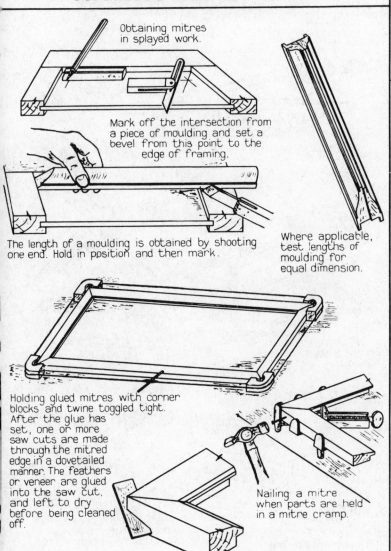

Obtaining mitres in splayed work.

Mark off the intersection from a piece of moulding and set a bevel from this point to the edge of framing.

The length of a moulding is obtained by shooting one end. Hold in position and then mark.

Where applicable, test lengths of moulding for equal dimension.

Holding glued mitres with corner blocks and twine toggled tight. After the glue has set, one or more saw cuts are made through the mitred edge in a dovetailed manner. The feathers or veneer are glued into the saw cut, and left to dry before being cleaned off.

Nailing a mitre when parts are held in a mitre cramp.

MITRE CUTS AND SHOOTS

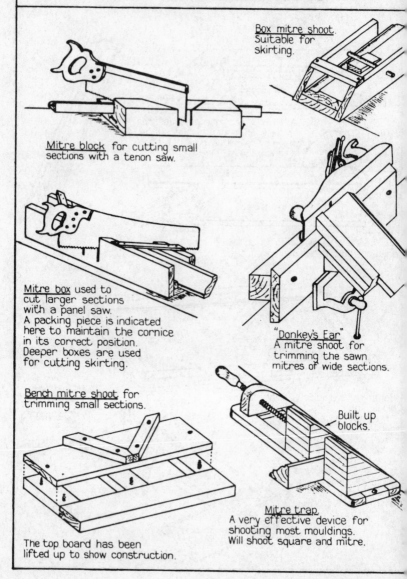

Box mitre shoot.
Suitable for
skirting.

Mitre block for cutting small
sections with a tenon saw.

Mitre box used to
cut larger sections
with a panel saw.
A packing piece is indicated
here to maintain the cornice
in its correct position.
Deeper boxes are used
for cutting skirting.

"Donkey's Ear"
A mitre shoot for
trimming the sawn
mitres of wide sections.

Bench mitre shoot for
trimming small sections.

Built up
blocks.

Mitre trap
A very effective device for
shooting most mouldings.
Will shoot square and mitre.

The top board has been
lifted up to show construction.

SLOT AND POCKET SCREWING

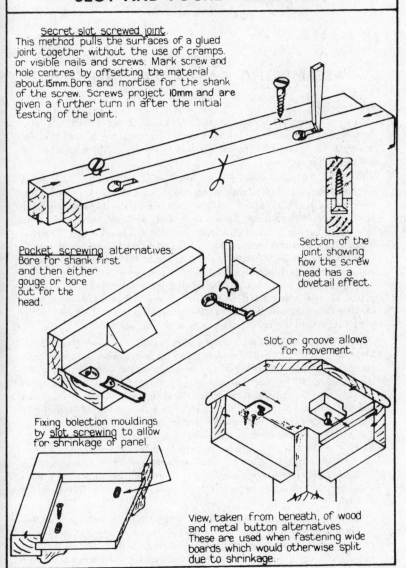

Secret slot screwed joint.
This method pulls the surfaces of a glued
joint together without the use of cramps.
or visible nails and screws. Mark screw and
hole centres by offsetting the material
about.15mm.Bore and mortise for the shank
of the screw. Screws project 10mm and are
given a further turn in after the initial
testing of the joint.

Section of the
joint showing
how the screw
head has a
dovetail effect.

Pocket screwing alternatives.
Bore for shank first
and then either
gouge or bore
out for the
head.

Slot or groove allows
for movement.

Fixing bolection mouldings
by slot screwing to allow
for shrinkage of panel.

View, taken from beneath, of wood
and metal button alternatives
These are used when fastening wide
boards which would otherwise split
due to shrinkage.

ASSEMBLING AND CLEANING OFF

ADHESIVES

THE term gluing has become accepted as meaning the operation whereby pieces of timber can be joined together by using one of a wide range of adhesives. Some have special qualities which make them suitable for particular types of work.

Animal glue. This glue is suitable for work which will not be subjected to wet conditions. It is available in various dried and undried forms. The former requires to be soaked in water for a period, depending on the size of the pieces, before being heated in a water-jacketed vessel, this is no more than having a tin of glue in a saucepan of heated water. The glue must not be in direct contact with heat and never exceed about 140°F. This temperature incidentally is about as hot as a finger will comfortably stand when dipped into the glue.

The resulting glue should flow readily from a brush but not to the extent that it is like water. Apply in a warm atmosphere away from chilling draughts which would cause the glue to gel and so prevent its penetration into the cellular structure of the timber.

Casein. Adhesives of this type are often known as 'cold water glues'. They are semi-durable and will therefore stand up to damp conditions but not excessive wetting. Obtained in powdered form, the adhesive has to be mixed in water to a paste-like consistency, then having stood for a short while, it can be thinned if necessary. Bear in mind that only a limited amount should be prepared for a day's use as in the mixed state it will commence to harden. Apply with a fibre brush or a flat stick. The atmospheric conditions are not important as there is no fear of chilling, making it ideal for application where large areas are involved. The standard casein has a staining effect on timber which is a disadvantage if the finished job is not painted. To overcome this difficulty a non-staining variety is manufactured for use with woods that will be polished or varnished.

Synthetic resin. In this range there are several types which have water-resistant qualities. One type comprises two separate applications—resin to, say, a mortise and the hardener, which is an acid, to the tenon. The act of bringing these two parts into contact causes a chemical change and setting takes place. Various setting times are available depending on the hardener chosen.

Other varieties are supplied in powder form with or without the hardening agent incorporated. To reconstitute, the powder is mixed with water, thus producing a resinous-like substance. The storage life of prepared resin is limited, but in the powder form it has a longer life. Adhere to makers' instructions rigidly when using these adhesives. Those who are subject to skin ailments should take adequate precautions.

Impact adhesive. This type of adhesive has its own particular uses, such as where sheets or strips of thin material have to be bonded to some form of rigid backing or base. Both surfaces are evenly coated with the adhesive and allowed to dry for a short while. Makers' instructions should be followed on this point as temperature has a bearing on the length of time between application and the bringing together of both surfaces. Care must be taken to accurately position the parts as there is no second chance once the adhesives have made contact. Air must be excluded as the joint is made and hammering on a block of wood will help in this respect and ensure a good bond.

With all 'gluing up' operations the pieces being joined should be clean and dry. A roughened surface will have greater holding power than a smooth one. This is the reason why toothed or sawn surfaces are preferred to planed ones.

Stale glue lacks strength and should not be used. Often dirty utensils or brushes will cause an adhesive to 'go off'. Cleanliness is an essential part of the assembly operation. Arrange beforehand all the necessary cramps, wedges, nails, and screws, etc., that are required before starting to glue up.

FITTING UP FRAMING

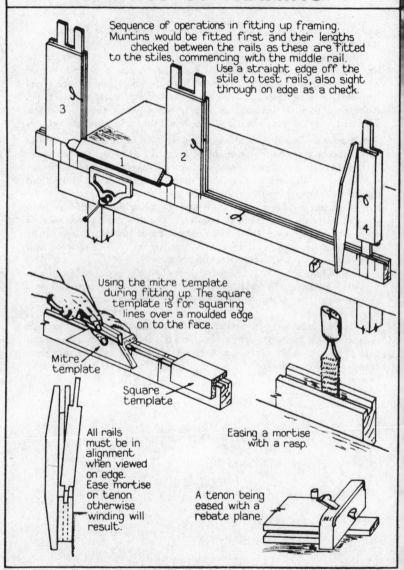

Sequence of operations in fitting up framing.
Muntins would be fitted first and their lengths
checked between the rails as these are fitted
to the stiles, commencing with the middle rail.

Use a straight edge off the
stile to test rails, also sight
through on edge as a check.

Using the mitre template
during fitting up. The square
template is for squaring
lines over a moulded edge
on to the face.

Mitre
template

Square
template

Easing a mortise
with a rasp.

All rails
must be in
alignment
when viewed
on edge.
Ease mortise
or tenon
otherwise
winding will
result.

A tenon being
eased with a
rebate plane.

GLUING UP

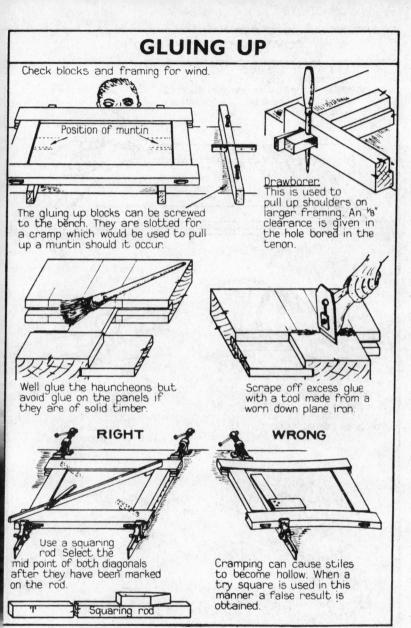

Check blocks and framing for wind.

Position of muntin

The gluing up blocks can be screwed to the bench. They are slotted for a cramp which would be used to pull up a muntin should it occur.

Drawborer
This is used to pull up shoulders on larger framing. An ⅛" clearance is given in the hole bored in the tenon.

Well glue the hauncheons but avoid glue on the panels if they are of solid timber.

Scrape off excess glue with a tool made from a worn down plane iron.

RIGHT

Use a squaring rod Select the mid point of both diagonals after they have been marked on the rod.

Squaring rod

WRONG

Cramping can cause stiles to become hollow. When a try square is used in this manner a false result is obtained.

CLEANING OFF ASSEMBLED JOBS

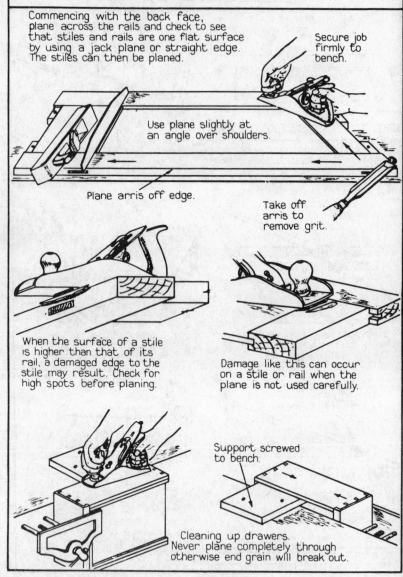

Commencing with the back face, plane across the rails and check to see that stiles and rails are one flat surface by using a jack plane or straight edge. The stiles can then be planed.

Secure job firmly to bench.

Use plane slightly at an angle over shoulders.

Plane arris off edge.

Take off arris to remove grit.

When the surface of a stile is higher than that of its rail, a damaged edge to the stile may result. Check for high spots before planing.

Damage like this can occur on a stile or rail when the plane is not used carefully.

Support screwed to bench.

Cleaning up drawers. Never plane completely through otherwise end grain will break out.

CABINET SCRAPER IN USE

Two views showing the method
of pushing the scraper.

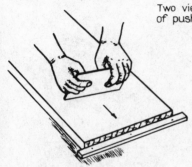

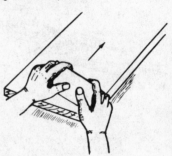

Drawing the scraper
towards oneself

Using the sweeping action
in front of the body method.

Two types of
<u>SCRAPER PLANE</u>

Sharpen edge of scraper
as for a plane iron to
angle "a".

Turn edge with the
burnisher using
angle "b".

Angle "c" is adjustable in the plane.

SHARPENING CABINET SCRAPER

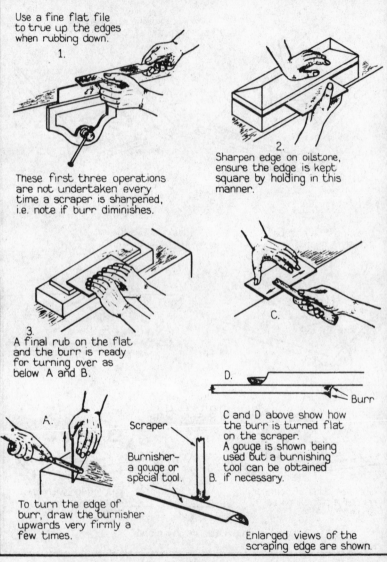

Use a fine flat file to true up the edges when rubbing down.

1.

These first three operations are not undertaken every time a scraper is sharpened, i.e. note if burr diminishes.

2.
Sharpen edge on oilstone, ensure the edge is kept square by holding in this manner.

C.

3.
A final rub on the flat and the burr is ready for turning over as below A and B.

A.

To turn the edge of burr, draw the burnisher upwards very firmly a few times.

Scraper

Burnisher— a gouge or special tool.

B.

D.

Burr

C and D above show how the burr is turned flat on the scraper. A gouge is shown being used but a burnishing tool can be obtained if necessary.

Enlarged views of the scraping edge are shown.

GLASSPAPERING

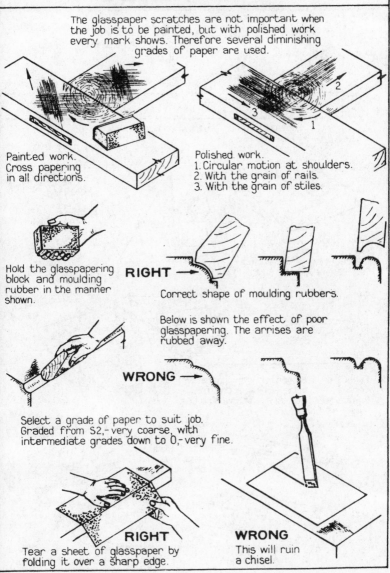

The glasspaper scratches are not important when the job is to be painted, but with polished work every mark shows. Therefore several diminishing grades of paper are used.

Painted work.
Cross papering
in all directions.

Polished work.
1. Circular motion at shoulders.
2. With the grain of rails.
3. With the grain of stiles.

Hold the glasspapering block and moulding rubber in the manner shown.

RIGHT ➔

Correct shape of moulding rubbers.

Below is shown the effect of poor glasspapering. The arrises are rubbed away.

WRONG ➔

Select a grade of paper to suit job. Graded from S2,- very coarse, with intermediate grades down to 0,- very fine.

RIGHT
Tear a sheet of glasspaper by folding it over a sharp edge.

WRONG
This will ruin a chisel.

PELLET, INSETS, AND OTHER REPAIRS

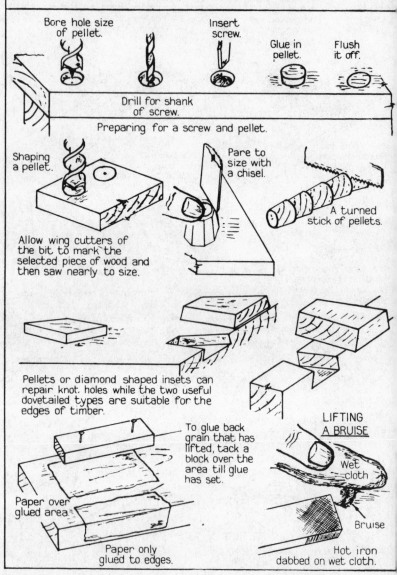

Bore hole size of pellet.

Insert screw.

Glue in pellet.

Flush it off.

Drill for shank of screw.

Preparing for a screw and pellet.

Shaping a pellet.

Pare to size with a chisel.

A turned stick of pellets.

Allow wing cutters of the bit to mark the selected piece of wood and then saw nearly to size.

Pellets or diamond shaped insets can repair knot holes while the two useful dovetailed types are suitable for the edges of timber.

To glue back grain that has lifted, tack a block over the area till glue has set.

LIFTING A BRUISE

Wet cloth

Bruise

Paper over glued area

Paper only glued to edges.

Hot iron dabbed on wet cloth.

104

IRONMONGERY—ASSOCIATED TOOLS AND OPERATIONS

SELECTION OF IRONMONGERY

OFTEN referred to as hardware; the merchant concerned deals with various forms of metal or plastic fastenings, locks and fixings etc., under this heading.

The selection of the correct metal or fitting for a particular purpose is important. Non-ferrous metals, such as brass and bronze, are particularly preferred where damp conditions will prevail, or for use with oak as the acid present in the timber would cause staining and corrosion if iron was used. Iron can be coated by one of a number of processes such as galvanizing or sherardizing. These prolong the life of iron considerably.

The better class of goods are usually manufactured from the range of non-ferrous metals and, for this reason, are incorporated into jobs where a good appearance is required, this being especially so with hardwoods.

Where moving parts are involved, such as locks, obtain the best possible. It is false economy to save money on these items when wear or corrosion will become apparent in a short time.

When choosing some hardware articles, a factor to be borne in mind is whether the item can be used on either hand—double handed—or only on the right or left hand. To cover every aspect of handing is not the purpose of this book, but the hand of the rising butt and locks illustrated have been stated as a general guide to this problem.

NAILS AND NAILING

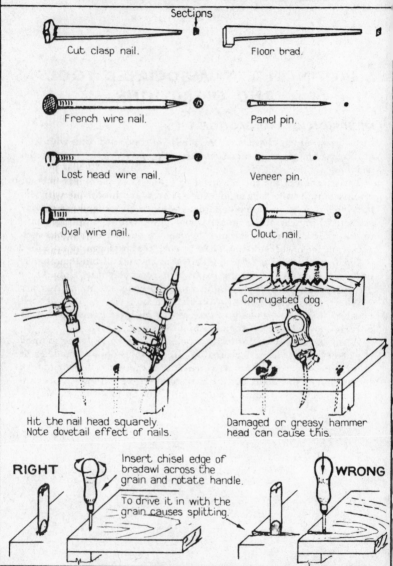

Sections

Cut clasp nail.

Floor brad.

French wire nail.

Panel pin.

Lost head wire nail.

Veneer pin.

Oval wire nail.

Clout nail.

Corrugated dog.

Hit the nail head squarely.
Note dovetail effect of nails.

Damaged or greasy hammer
head can cause this.

RIGHT

Insert chisel edge of
bradawl across the
grain and rotate handle.

To drive it in with the
grain causes splitting.

WRONG

POSITIONING NAILS

RIGHT	WRONG

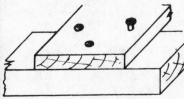

Method of arranging nails to prevent splitting.

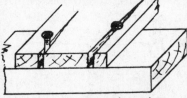

Nails too near the end or edge of timber cause splitting

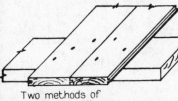

Two methods of staggering nails.

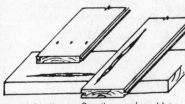

Straight lines of nails weaken the timber and cause it to split.

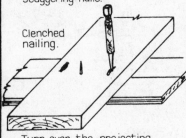

Clenched nailing.

Turn over the projecting part of nail with the grain and punch below surface.

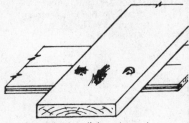

An unpointed nail breaks out the timber. Unsightly when nail is turned over across the grain.

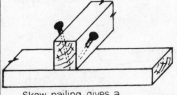

Skew nailing gives a dovetailed effect and is therefore strong.

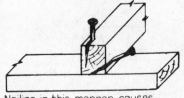

Nailing in this manner causes the wood to split and a loss in strength.

HAMMERS

Hammer handles are of straight grained ash, or hickory.

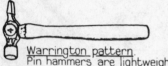

Warrington pattern.
Pin hammers are lightweight types.

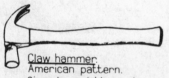

London pattern.
Sizes of above by numbers 0 to 8.

Secure the head with glued wedges. Barbed metal wedges can also be used.

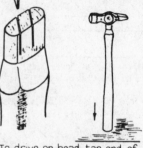

To drive on head, tap end of handle on something firm.

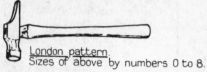

Claw hammer.
American pattern.
Sizes by weight ranging from 13 oz. to 28 oz.
An average weight is 20 oz.

RIGHT

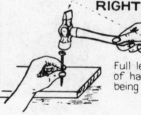

Full length of handle being used.

WRONG

Restricted movement and no force to a blow.

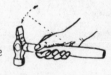

When using the claw hammer to withdraw nails avoid excessive force or the handle is likely to fracture at the head.

Clean the face of the hammer fairly often on a worn piece of glasspaper.

PINCERS

Two patterns of pincers.

The jaws should be capable of cutting up to 1½" wire nails.

This 152-200mm type with plain arms is to be prefered to that shown below.

It is their ability to cut into a nail that prevents them slipping.

The tack lifter on one arm and a ball on the other make this pincer uncomfortable to the hand when gripping with considerable force.

Limited amount of pull when relying on the head for grip.

RIGHT

Protection piece

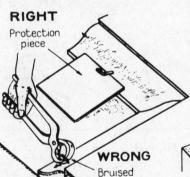

WRONG

Bruised moulding

To prevent damage to the timber when pulling out nails, place a scraper or piece of hardboard under the head of the pincer.

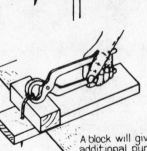

A block will give an additional purchase to the pincer.

SCREWS AND CUPS

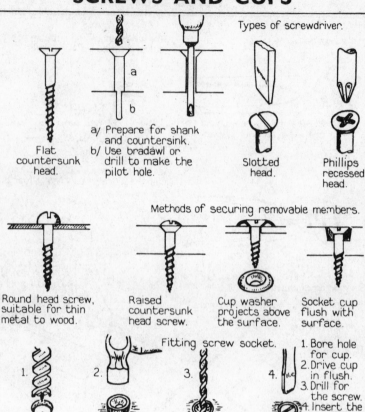

Flat countersunk head.

a/ Prepare for shank and countersink.
b/ Use bradawl or drill to make the pilot hole.

Types of screwdriver.

Slotted head.

Phillips recessed head.

Methods of securing removable members.

Round head screw, suitable for thin metal to wood.

Raised countersunk head screw.

Cup washer projects above the surface.

Socket cup flush with surface.

Fitting screw socket.

1.
2.
3.
4.

1. Bore hole for cup.
2. Drive cup in flush.
3. Drill for the screw.
4. Insert the screw.

WRONG

WRONG

Shank holes drilled incorrectly.

Broken head caused by a hammer.

Too large – screw bites into wood.

Too small – results in burred head. Keep fingers away from burrs.

SCREWDRIVER

An 8" and 4" screwdriver will do most work, a 12" for large screws.

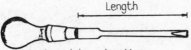

Oval registered pattern.

London pattern.

Ratchet type.

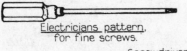

Electricians pattern, for fine screws.

Screwdriver bit.

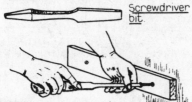

a. b.

WRONG

a/ The end of the screwdriver is too thick and will burr the head of screw.

b/ Here it is too thin and will twist.

Prepare a hole and countersink to suit the screw's shank and head.

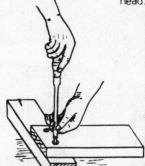

To insert screws, support or guide the screwdriver.

WRONG

Screwdriver damages work if too large.

Do not lever with a screwdriver as it will easily bend.

Screwdriver too small.

FITTING BUTT HINGES

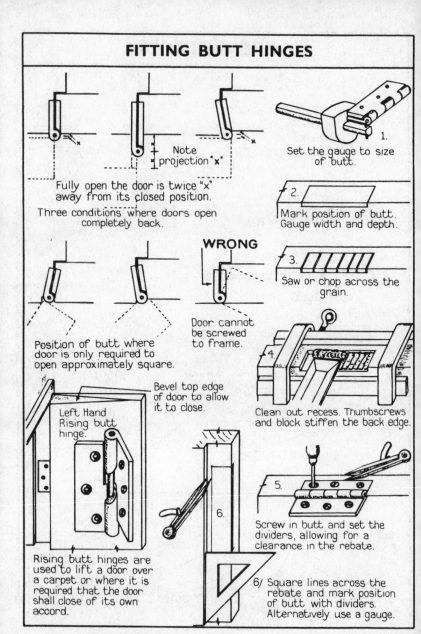

Note projection "x"

Fully open the door is twice "x" away from its closed position.

Three conditions where doors open completely back.

WRONG

Position of butt where door is only required to open approximately square.

Door cannot be screwed to frame.

Bevel top edge of door to allow it to close.

Left Hand Rising butt hinge.

Rising butt hinges are used to lift a door over a carpet or where it is required that the door shall close of its own accord.

1. Set the gauge to size of butt.

2. Mark position of butt. Gauge width and depth.

3. Saw or chop across the grain.

4. Clean out recess. Thumbscrews and block stiffen the back edge.

5. Screw in butt and set the dividers, allowing for a clearance in the rebate.

6. Square lines across the rebate and mark position of butt with dividers. Alternatively use a gauge.

MORTISE, RIM, AND CUPBOARD LOCKS

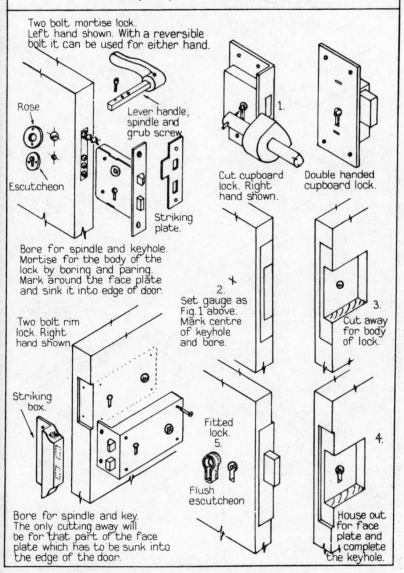

Two bolt mortise lock.
Left hand shown. With a reversible
bolt it can be used for either hand.

Rose

Escutcheon

Lever handle,
spindle and
grub screw

Striking
plate.

Bore for spindle and keyhole.
Mortise for the body of the
lock by boring and paring.
Mark around the face plate
and sink it into edge of door.

Two bolt rim
lock. Right
hand shown.

Striking
box.

Bore for spindle and key.
The only cutting away will
be for that part of the face
plate which has to be sunk into
the edge of the door.

1.

Cut cupboard
lock. Right
hand shown.

Double handed
cupboard lock.

2.
Set gauge as
Fig.1 above.
Mark centre
of keyhole
and bore.

3.
Cut away
for body
of lock.

Fitted
lock.
5.

Flush
escutcheon

4.

House out
for face
plate and
complete
the keyhole.

HANDRAIL AND COACH SCREWS OR BOLTS

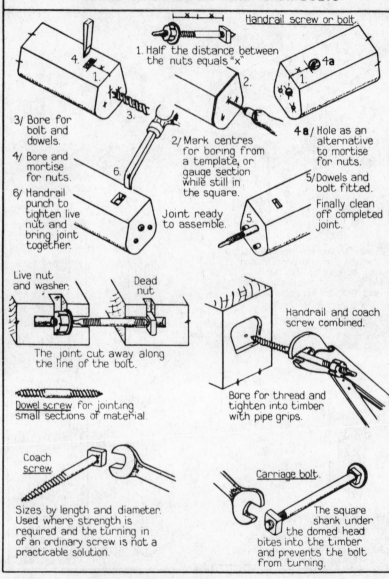

Handrail screw or bolt.

1. Half the distance between the nuts equals "x"

3/ Bore for bolt and dowels.

4/ Bore and mortise for nuts.

6/ Handrail punch to tighten live nut and bring joint together.

2/ Mark centres for boring from a template, or gauge section while still in the square.

Joint ready to assemble.

4a/ Hole as an alternative to mortise for nuts.

5/ Dowels and bolt fitted.

Finally clean off completed joint.

Live nut and washer.

Dead nut

The joint cut away along the line of the bolt.

Dowel screw for jointing small sections of material.

Handrail and coach screw combined.

Bore for thread and tighten into timber with pipe grips.

Coach screw.

Sizes by length and diameter. Used where strength is required and the turning in of an ordinary screw is not a practicable solution.

Carriage bolt.

The square shank under the domed head bites into the timber and prevents the bolt from turning.

WALL PLUGGING

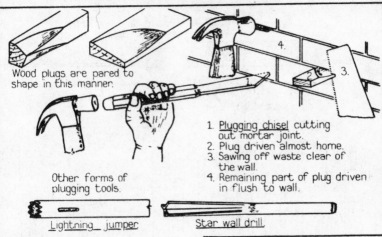

Wood plugs are pared to shape in this manner.

Other forms of plugging tools.

1. Plugging chisel cutting out mortar joint.
2. Plug driven almost home.
3. Sawing off waste clear of the wall.
4. Remaining part of plug driven in flush to wall.

Lightning jumper

Star wall drill

Numerous fixing devices have also been developed for use in conjunction with materials other than the ordinary brick and plastered wall illustrated.

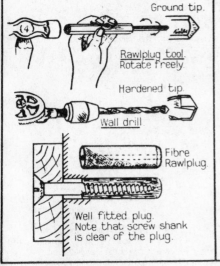

Ground tip.

Rawlplug tool. Rotate freely.

Hardened tip.

Wall drill.

Fibre Rawlplug.

Well fitted plug. Note that screw shank is clear of the plug.

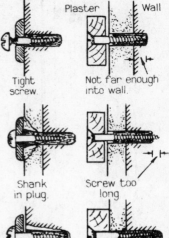

WRONG

Plaster   Wall

Tight screw.

Not far enough into wall.

Shank in plug.

Screw too long

Irregular hole.

Screw not in centre of plug.

LEVELLING AND PLUMBING OPERATIONS

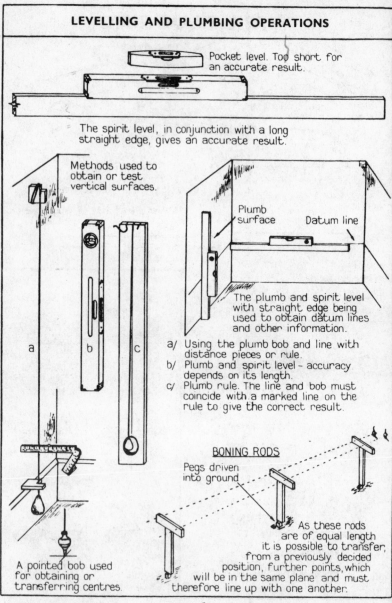

Pocket level. Too short for an accurate result.

The spirit level, in conjunction with a long straight edge, gives an accurate result.

Methods used to obtain or test vertical surfaces.

Plumb surface

Datum line

The plumb and spirit level with straight edge being used to obtain datum lines and other information.

a/ Using the plumb bob and line with distance pieces or rule.
b/ Plumb and spirit level – accuracy depends on its length.
c/ Plumb rule. The line and bob must coincide with a marked line on the rule to give the correct result.

a   b   c

BONING RODS

Pegs driven into ground

As these rods are of equal length it is possible to transfer from a previously decided position, further points, which will be in the same plane and must therefore line up with one another.

A pointed bob used for obtaining or transferring centres.